WOOD-FRAMED SHEAR WALL CONSTRUCTION

AN ILLUSTRATED GUIDE
2ND EDITION

THOR MATTESON, S.E.

INTERNATIONAL
CODE COUNCIL

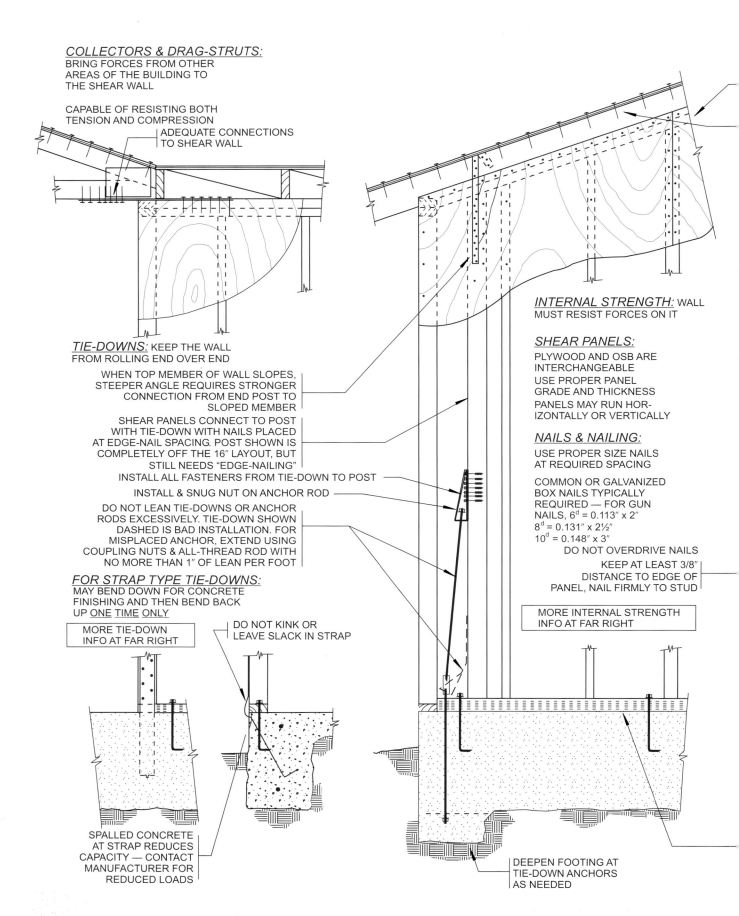

COLLECTORS & DRAG-STRUTS:
BRING FORCES FROM OTHER
AREAS OF THE BUILDING TO
THE SHEAR WALL

CAPABLE OF RESISTING BOTH
TENSION AND COMPRESSION

ADEQUATE CONNECTIONS
TO SHEAR WALL

TIE-DOWNS: KEEP THE WALL
FROM ROLLING END OVER END

WHEN TOP MEMBER OF WALL SLOPES,
STEEPER ANGLE REQUIRES STRONGER
CONNECTION FROM END POST TO
SLOPED MEMBER

SHEAR PANELS CONNECT TO POST
WITH TIE-DOWN WITH NAILS PLACED
AT EDGE-NAIL SPACING. POST SHOWN IS
COMPLETELY OFF THE 16″ LAYOUT, BUT
STILL NEEDS "EDGE-NAILING"

INSTALL ALL FASTENERS FROM TIE-DOWN TO POST

INSTALL & SNUG NUT ON ANCHOR ROD

DO NOT LEAN TIE-DOWNS OR ANCHOR
RODS EXCESSIVELY. TIE-DOWN SHOWN
DASHED IS BAD INSTALLATION. FOR
MISPLACED ANCHOR, EXTEND USING
COUPLING NUTS & ALL-THREAD ROD WITH
NO MORE THAN 1″ OF LEAN PER FOOT

FOR STRAP TYPE TIE-DOWNS:
MAY BEND DOWN FOR CONCRETE
FINISHING AND THEN BEND BACK
UP ONE TIME ONLY

MORE TIE-DOWN
INFO AT FAR RIGHT

DO NOT KINK OR
LEAVE SLACK IN STRAP

SPALLED CONCRETE
AT STRAP REDUCES
CAPACITY — CONTACT
MANUFACTURER FOR
REDUCED LOADS

INTERNAL STRENGTH: WALL
MUST RESIST FORCES ON IT

SHEAR PANELS:
PLYWOOD AND OSB ARE
INTERCHANGEABLE
USE PROPER PANEL
GRADE AND THICKNESS
PANELS MAY RUN HOR-
IZONTALLY OR VERTICALLY

NAILS & NAILING:
USE PROPER SIZE NAILS
AT REQUIRED SPACING

COMMON OR GALVANIZED
BOX NAILS TYPICALLY
REQUIRED — FOR GUN
NAILS, 6^d = 0.113″ x 2″
8^d = 0.131″ x 2½″
10^d = 0.148″ x 3″
DO NOT OVERDRIVE NAILS
KEEP AT LEAST 3/8″
DISTANCE TO EDGE OF
PANEL, NAIL FIRMLY TO STUD

MORE INTERNAL STRENGTH
INFO AT FAR RIGHT

DEEPEN FOOTING AT
TIE-DOWN ANCHORS
AS NEEDED

SHEAR WALL "QUICK START"

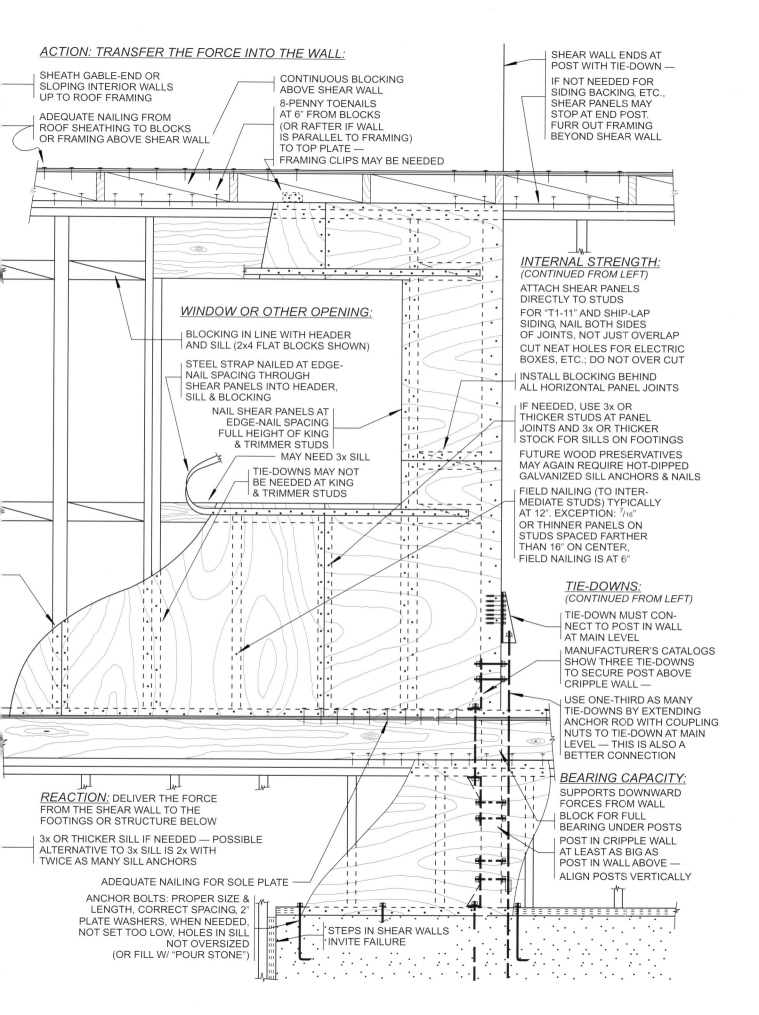

ACTION: TRANSFER THE FORCE INTO THE WALL:

SHEATH GABLE-END OR SLOPING INTERIOR WALLS UP TO ROOF FRAMING

ADEQUATE NAILING FROM ROOF SHEATHING TO BLOCKS OR FRAMING ABOVE SHEAR WALL

CONTINUOUS BLOCKING ABOVE SHEAR WALL
8-PENNY TOENAILS AT 6″ FROM BLOCKS (OR RAFTER IF WALL IS PARALLEL TO FRAMING) TO TOP PLATE — FRAMING CLIPS MAY BE NEEDED

SHEAR WALL ENDS AT POST WITH TIE-DOWN —

IF NOT NEEDED FOR SIDING BACKING, ETC., SHEAR PANELS MAY STOP AT END POST. FURR OUT FRAMING BEYOND SHEAR WALL

WINDOW OR OTHER OPENING:

BLOCKING IN LINE WITH HEADER AND SILL (2x4 FLAT BLOCKS SHOWN)

STEEL STRAP NAILED AT EDGE-NAIL SPACING THROUGH SHEAR PANELS INTO HEADER, SILL & BLOCKING

NAIL SHEAR PANELS AT EDGE-NAIL SPACING FULL HEIGHT OF KING & TRIMMER STUDS

MAY NEED 3x SILL

TIE-DOWNS MAY NOT BE NEEDED AT KING & TRIMMER STUDS

INTERNAL STRENGTH:
(CONTINUED FROM LEFT)

ATTACH SHEAR PANELS DIRECTLY TO STUDS

FOR "T1-11" AND SHIP-LAP SIDING, NAIL BOTH SIDES OF JOINTS, NOT JUST OVERLAP

CUT NEAT HOLES FOR ELECTRIC BOXES, ETC.; DO NOT OVER CUT

INSTALL BLOCKING BEHIND ALL HORIZONTAL PANEL JOINTS

IF NEEDED, USE 3x OR THICKER STUDS AT PANEL JOINTS AND 3x OR THICKER STOCK FOR SILLS ON FOOTINGS

FUTURE WOOD PRESERVATIVES MAY AGAIN REQUIRE HOT-DIPPED GALVANIZED SILL ANCHORS & NAILS

FIELD NAILING (TO INTER-MEDIATE STUDS) TYPICALLY AT 12″. EXCEPTION: $^7/_{16}$″ OR THINNER PANELS ON STUDS SPACED FARTHER THAN 16″ ON CENTER, FIELD NAILING IS AT 6″

TIE-DOWNS:
(CONTINUED FROM LEFT)

TIE-DOWN MUST CON-NECT TO POST IN WALL AT MAIN LEVEL

MANUFACTURER'S CATALOGS SHOW THREE TIE-DOWNS TO SECURE POST ABOVE CRIPPLE WALL —

USE ONE-THIRD AS MANY TIE-DOWNS BY EXTENDING ANCHOR ROD WITH COUPLING NUTS TO TIE-DOWN AT MAIN LEVEL — THIS IS ALSO A BETTER CONNECTION

BEARING CAPACITY:
SUPPORTS DOWNWARD FORCES FROM WALL
BLOCK FOR FULL BEARING UNDER POSTS
POST IN CRIPPLE WALL AT LEAST AS BIG AS POST IN WALL ABOVE — ALIGN POSTS VERTICALLY

REACTION: DELIVER THE FORCE FROM THE SHEAR WALL TO THE FOOTINGS OR STRUCTURE BELOW

3x OR THICKER SILL IF NEEDED — POSSIBLE ALTERNATIVE TO 3x SILL IS 2x WITH TWICE AS MANY SILL ANCHORS

ADEQUATE NAILING FOR SOLE PLATE

ANCHOR BOLTS: PROPER SIZE & LENGTH, CORRECT SPACING, 2″ PLATE WASHERS, WHEN NEEDED, NOT SET TOO LOW, HOLES IN SILL NOT OVERSIZED (OR FILL W/ "POUR STONE")

STEPS IN SHEAR WALLS INVITE FAILURE

WOOD-FRAMED SHEAR WALL CONSTRUCTION

An Illustrated Guide

ISBN # 978-1-58001-996-5

COPYRIGHT © 2011
by
INTERNATIONAL CODE COUNCIL, INC.

Errata on various ICC publications may be available at www.iccsafe.org/errata.

First Printing: September 2011

Printed in the United States of America

PREFACE

This book gives carpenters and others interested in wood-framed construction an understanding of one of the most important structural components in today's framed buildings: the wood-framed shear wall. As a structural engineer and former carpenter, I have many years of experience designing and building residential and light commercial construction. I began to wonder why I kept seeing the same shear wall problems repeated throughout the West and offered to give a talk to the local contractors association on shear wall basics. While preparing for this presentation, I looked for references for those seeking more information on shear walls. I reviewed dozens of books on carpentry and construction but did not turn up anything addressing many of the conditions carpenters often face in the field. Engineers, however, have many resources on shear wall design. I present much of this knowledge in terms that will make sense to builders.

This guide fills the void between what engineers always thought carpenters knew and what current publications actually present about shear wall construction. Most engineers will also find useful information that I have gathered from many sources. Engineers can also benefit from seeing the real-life examples of shear wall construction, both good and bad, shown throughout the book.

The opinions, views and conclusions expressed in this guide are solely those of the author and not necessarily those of the International Code Council®. Although specific products, brands and services are discussed or shown in this guide, it is not the intent of the author or the International Code Council® to endorse any particular product or service.

INTRODUCTION

The first sections of this guide cover the basic principles of shear walls. Reading these sections will not make you an engineer but will introduce you to the essential five aspects in any shear wall. If you already understand how shear walls function (or maybe you don't care, you just need to build one now and ask questions later), you may wish to turn directly to the "nuts and bolts" part of the guide. Chapter 3, "Basic Shear Wall Construction Requirements and Solutions," covers many situations carpenters encounter while building shear walls, including some methods to correct common problems. The Quick Start figure on the inside cover illustrates many basic shear wall requirements. Chapters 4 and 5 introduce related and advanced topics including collectors and shear wall reinforcement around openings.

Chapter 6 is new to this edition and presents an introduction to earthquake retrofits for typical older homes in earthquake-prone areas that are built on cripple walls or crawlspace foundations. This topic could easily fill an entire book by itself, but until that book is written I wanted to present the basics—hopefully in time for readers to prepare before the next devastating earthquake.

Although I often refer to residential construction in this guide, wood-framed shear walls behave the same in any wood-framed building. The information in this book applies just as well to residential as it does to light commercial or institutional buildings. After all, the shear wall does not care what type of building it's in—it only cares if it's built correctly when an earthquake or windstorm comes along.

Authors—myself included—sometimes get so wrapped up in presenting a specific topic that they miss important details or present information in a way that can mislead the reader. Though subject matter that appears in a photograph may illustrate the author's point, readers might notice other features in the photo that apply only in certain situations, were not completed at the time the photo was taken or are just plain wrong. Beware of focusing on something besides the topic directly presented in this guide or any other.

I never dreamed that I could write over 100 pages about shear walls, and yet this guide is only the beginning of the information I hope to provide. Many readers will have questions not covered here or will have points that they would like clarified. You can find a much more dynamic source of information at http://www.shearwalls.com. This website includes answers to frequently asked questions, links to hardware manufacturers, building code clarifications and updates, and the opportunity to submit your own questions.

ACKNOWLEDGMENTS

It has been a great privilege to work with so many prominent contractors, engineers and other experts during the course of this project. Thanks to all who inspired and influenced this book, and especially to the following reviewers:

Jeff Bailey & Howard Cook
Bay Area Retrofit
737 Page Street, Berkeley, CA 94710

Dave Barrowcliffe Building Contractor
16 Woodstock Street
Maryborough, Queensland 4650
Australia

Ian Cadell
812 Kirner Rd.
Sequim, WA   98382

Charles Campbell

Jesse Christensen
Josh Christensen
Christensen Brothers Construction, Inc.
2531 Watson Street
Castro Valley, CA   94546

Bruce D. Clayton, Ph.D.
Independent Technical Author
P.O. Box 1194
Mariposa, CA   95338

Alfred Commins
Commins Manufacturing Inc
960B Guard Street
Friday Harbor, WA   98250

Burt Collins,
General Contractor
P.O. Box 161
Mariposa, CA   95338

Theodore L. Droessler, P.E.
Principal Engineer
Clark Co Dept of Development Services
Building Division
4701 W. Russell Road
Las Vegas, NV   89118

John Gardner
Gardner Estimating Services
2310 Claassen Ranch Lane
Paso Robles, CA   93446

Ronald F. "Rawn" Nelson
R. F. Nelson & Associates
Consulting Structural Engineers
840 20th Street
Hermosa Beach, CA   90254

Nels Roselund, Structural Engineer
Roselund Engineering Company
8453 Yarrow Street
Rosemead, CA   91770

Ben Schmid
Consulting Structural Engineer
203 Pearl Avenue
Balboa Island, CA   92622

Kathryn Sedwick, Structural Engineer
City of San Jose Building Division
801 N. First Street, Room 200
San Jose, CA   95110

Dick Seibert
General Contractor
1603 Silverwood Drive
Martinez, CA   94553

John G. Shipp
ABS Consulting
300 Commerce Drive, Suite 200
Irvine, CA   92602

Douglas Thompson, SE
STB Structural Engineers, Inc.
21084 Bake Parkway, Suite 100
Lake Forest, CA   92630

Danny Waite
Pine Ridge Builders
P.O. Box 661
Graham, WA   98338

TABLE OF CONTENTS

Chapter 1

BACKGROUND INFORMATION

If you already know the basic mechanics of shear walls and need specific information on installation requirements, you may want to go directly to Chapter 3, "Basic Shear Wall Construction Requirements and Solutions," on Page 27. The reader of this guide is expected to know basic terms used in wood-framed construction. Still, many of these terms are listed in the Glossary. For terms not listed, a references section on wood-framed construction has been provided.

PURPOSE OF SHEAR WALLS

Designers must consider two kinds of loads: vertical loads and lateral loads. Vertical loads come from the weight of the building and its contents (dead and live loads, respectively), and sometimes rain, ice or snow. Lateral loads act horizontally on the building.

1.1.1 Shear walls resist loads that act horizontally

Earthquake and wind forces typically produce the lateral loads designers must consider, though occasionally designers must also consider such horizontal forces as floodwater or pressure from earth banks against buildings. Shear walls typically only "feel" lateral loads when wind and earthquake forces act on a building.

1.1.2 What shear walls do *not* do

Shear walls do not necessarily support vertical loads; bearing walls support vertical loads. If a bearing wall has also been sheathed with shear panels, the studs carry vertical loads, but the shear panels just sit there waiting for an earthquake or hurricane to occur. Until something applies a lateral load on the building, the sheathing does nothing.

A load-bearing wall can support heavy vertical loads and still have no ability to resist lateral forces. You could build a three-story house and stack gold bricks waist deep on each floor. As long as the posts, beams, bearing walls, floor joists and so forth were strong enough, the house could stand up without any shear walls or other bracing—until an earthquake or wind storm came along.

WHY SHEAR WALLS MATTER

Why are shear walls so important? We build shear walls to keep buildings from suffering major damage in that freak storm or earthquake that may not even occur in the lifetime of a structure. On the other hand, either of these events could occur before you finish reading this book. Building codes require designing for these unusual events because they could be so devastating that substandard structures would collapse into piles of debris—possibly with their occupants inside. Shear walls are like airbags in your car: It's nice to know they are there, but you hope you never really need them.

Why focus on the shear walls instead of all the other components in the system? Because lateral forces collected by many small members and connections spread over a large area concentrate at shear walls. Many custom homes depend on just a few shear walls to protect them against damage in an earthquake or windstorm. The rest of the exterior may be windows, doors or walls that step in and out around bays and recesses. Such designs do not provide adequate stability for the house to withstand lateral loads without carefully designed and constructed shear walls.

SOME MISCONCEPTIONS ABOUT SHEAR WALLS

Myth #1: **You only need shear walls if you live near an earthquake fault**

One of the biggest misconceptions about shear walls is that they are only needed in earthquake country. Even in the worst seismic regions, wind pressures often produce the greatest forces in wood-framed buildings. The *International Building Code®* (IBC®) requires engineers in California to design for 85 mph (3 second gust) wind speed; along the east coast engineers design for wind speeds of 90 to 150 mph as you move south from Maine to Florida and the Gulf of Mexico.

A scientist would say that wind pressure is proportional to the square of the wind speed. This just means that if the wind blows two times as fast, it pushes against a building four times as hard (two squared equals four); if the wind blows three times as fast, it pushes nine times as hard (three squared equals nine). Florida's 150 mph winds have nearly three times the force of New England's 90 mph winds.

The May/June 2001 issue of *Building Standards* magazine[1] reports that "high-wind events cause more fatalities and property damage than any other type of natural disaster, including earthquakes." So don't feel completely safe if you don't live in earthquake country.

Myth #2: **Sheathing all the exterior walls will provide enough strength**

When plywood first became widely used, sheathing the walls of a typical home usually gave it enough strength and stiffness to resist wind or earthquake forces. Occasionally, engineers see notes on plans by unlicensed designers that say something like, "shear entire house" (presumably meaning sheath the whole house with shear panels). While this might be adequate if you really did sheath the *entire* house—including over all the door and window openings—simply sheathing the outside walls of today's custom homes usually will not provide nearly the strength and stiffness needed. This is not because earthquakes or hurricanes have become more powerful or wood structural panels or plywood have become weaker, but rather because of the changes in architectural design from homes built 50 years ago.

Myth #3: **Shear walls will make your house earthquakeproof**

Another huge misconception is thinking that properly built shear walls will make your house earthquake-proof or hurricane-proof. The only earthquake-proof structure built to date is the International Space Station. The seismic design basis of the IBC is the National Earthquake Hazards Reduction Program (NEHRP) *Recommended Provisions for Seismic Regulations for New Buildings and Other Structures* published by the Building Seismic Safety Council. The NEHRP provisions are incorporated into the *Minimum Design Loads for Buildings and Other Structures* (ASCE 7) standard, which is the referenced standard for structural loads in the IBC. According to the NEHRP commentary, the goal of the seismic provisions is to provide criteria for the design and construction of new structures subject to earthquake ground motions that is intended to minimize the hazard to life for all structures. To that end, the IBC seismic requirements provide minimum criteria considered prudent for the protection of life safety in structures subject to earthquakes.

The building codes are written with the expectation that your house will survive the design earthquake without collapsing. The premise is that this big earthquake will be so devastating that your house could collapse and injure or kill you if it was not properly built to code. The same likelihood of a major windstorm is used to establish what wind forces to use in design. Meeting the requirements of the earthquake provisions means that a building's occupants will most likely survive, but the building may be a total loss! The "design event" could severely damage your house, but if it was built to the code expectation you would be alive to have it repaired at enormous expense, or bulldozed.

1.4

DAMAGE CONTROL VERSUS LIFE SAFETY

The 2009 IBC states in Section 101.3 that "the purpose of this code is to establish the minimum requirements to safeguard the public health, safety and general welfare. . . and safety to life and property. . . ." Protecting property goes beyond what the seismic design provisions of the code expect (as discussed in the previous section). One of the design requirements given in the code limits how much your building can sway back and forth (deflect, or "drift") during an earthquake. The code gives this story-drift limit (lateral sway) as a percentage of the height of each story in a building. For residences with typical 8-foot ceilings, the deflection limit is about 2 inches per story (two percent of the story height). Previous building codes limited the deflection to much smaller amounts (about $1/4$-inch per story). This stricter limitation was partly intended to reduce damage to building finishes such as stucco, plaster, gypsum drywall and tile. Recent research has found that an 8-foot-tall wall can deflect about $3/8$ inch without damaging the drywall finish. Previous building codes limited story drift so that damage to drywall would be limited.

The building codes list allowable design strengths for wood structural panel [plywood and oriented strand board (OSB)] shear walls. These strength values came from tests done by the American Plywood Association or "the APA" (now called "APA—The Engineered Wood Association"). The APA's test results gave values that occur when the walls have deflected much more than the $3/8$ inch per story mentioned above that would damage drywall. Although this strength level helps engineers design to prevent total collapse of a structure, it was not intended to keep buildings habitable after an earthquake.

Because the building codes were written collectively by hundreds of experts in dozens of different fields, different code sections do not always agree with each other. This could explain why one code section lets your house get destroyed in an earthquake, while another section protects it from damage. I would not want to have to explain to a jury why I ignored the provisions on page 1 of the code that require protection of property, and only supplied a design that gave basic life safety. Engineers should give much more consideration to limiting deflection and damage to buildings they design rather than focusing on building strength alone.

People usually come to an engineer saying, "Give me the minimum design needed to meet the code." While this may produce a design that will protect life and limb, it could leave the building vulnerable to severe property damage. Meeting the objective of safeguarding property in addition to life and limb requires more design work than simply meeting the minimum code requirements. Section 4.3.2 of the *Special Design Provisions for Wind and Seismic* (SDPWS—Reference 18) gives a way to determine how much a shear wall will deflect under a given lateral load. The SDPWS is adopted by reference as part of the 2009 IBC. (This information also appears in Reference 12, which, at the time of this writing, is available for free download at www.apawood.org.) With this information your designer can determine the shear wall construction needed to protect your house from suffering major damage during an earthquake.

Insurance helps cover monetary losses but will not reduce the anguish of losing your home, even temporarily. Furthermore, when a whole community suffers a disaster, the effects are far greater than isolated incidents of loss. Say you leave on vacation, forget to turn off your clothes iron, and your house burns to the ground. Your insurance company pays for a contractor to rebuild it, and you spend six months in a motel until it is finished. Now suppose an earthquake or hurricane destroys your house and many of the others in the area. Suddenly all the contractors in the region are very busy and cannot start rebuilding your house for over a year. Do you live in a motel for two years? Does your insurance policy provide for payment of housing costs for that long? Do you want your house built by crews that are rushing to finish up and move on to the next rebuild, or crews made up of less skilled "emergency" hires? Do you uproot your family and move to another community? After the 1994 Northridge earthquake, some people did live in motels for over two years, waiting for their houses to be rebuilt.

Insurance companies make up for huge payouts after disasters by raising their rates. Californians were still feeling ripples in their insurance premiums nearly a decade after the Northridge earthquake. If you have earthquake insurance in California, the typical deductible for damage is 10 to 15 percent of your home's value. Most people do not have this much money sitting in their bank accounts. An extremely conservative engineered design for your home would add about 10 percent to its construction cost; a reasonably thorough design might add only three to five percent. A well-designed and constructed house is simply another form of insurance and should look more appealing than being forced out of your house after a disaster.

WHY SO MUCH FUSS ABOUT SHEAR WALLS RECENTLY?

1.5.1 Changes in house designs have reduced the strength of modern homes

Recent disasters such as Hurricane Katrina in 2005, Hurricane Andrew in 1992 and the 1989 Loma Prieta and 1994 Northridge earthquakes in California caused more damage than expected. One factor in the increased damage level is the change in typical house layouts from 50 years ago. Older houses were divided into many rooms, whereas many newer (and most custom) homes have very open floor plans—the family room flows into the living room, which flows into the dining room and kitchen. All those separate rooms in an old house gave it strength, like a honeycomb. Figure 1 shows a sturdily built older home that survived rolling off a house-mover's trailer. Typical new houses do not have as many interior walls to give them that strength, and they have suffered for it. The Los Angeles Department of Building and Safety found that most of the damage in the Northridge earthquake occurred in homes built *after* 1970.[2]

As houses were built larger and more open, they also began to include more windows. Figure 2 illustrates a typical tract house from 50 years ago, whereas Figure 3 depicts a modern custom home. Custom homes often have exterior walls with many windows, which eliminate strength from those walls. At the same time, strength provided by interior walls has been reduced. The few walls present in a modern custom home must carry much larger forces than walls in older homes.

Figure 1

Don't try this with today's homes! This older home survived an accident that would have crumpled a modern structure. Used with permission of Thaddeus Holownia.

Figure 2

A typical older tract house had enough exterior wall length to provide strength.

Figure 3
Windows, bays and jogs in modern homes take strength away from the walls.

Building materials used in homes have changed over the decades as well. Some have gotten stronger. Wood structural panel sheathing such as plywood and OSB are much stronger than the plain lumber sheathing used before. Nails used in today's homes, however, typically do not provide the connection strength that older, "common" nails did in decades past (this is discussed at great length later in the book). Changes in building material weights also affect how buildings behave. Compared to a contemporary roof of concrete tile, a light cedar shake or shingle roof would not exert much force on the structure below during an earthquake.

1.5.2 Widespread earthquake and wind hazards

Figures 4 and 5 show seismic design and wind speed maps, respectively, that the 2009 IBC is based on. Very few areas in the United States are free from both wind and earthquake hazards. Michigan and South-central Texas appear relatively safe from these particular hazards—take your pick of freezing winters or scorching hot summers.

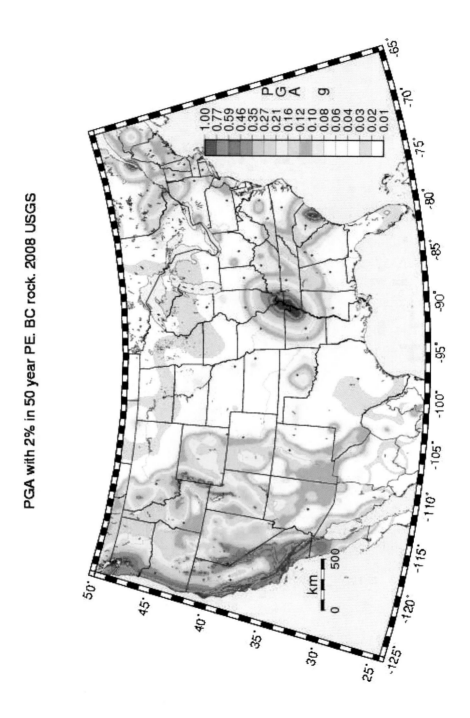

Figure 4
U.S. Geological Survey map of earthquake hazard areas.[3]

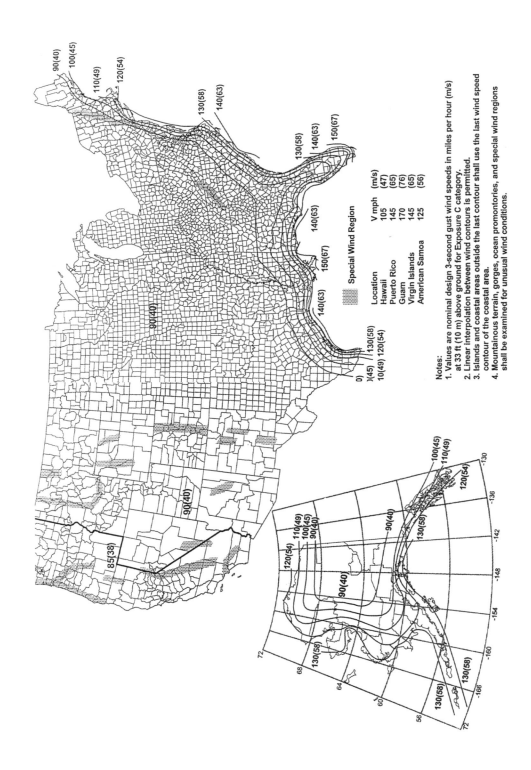

Figure 5
Wind-speed map as shown in the 2009 IBC.

SHEAR WALLS AND THE BUILDING CODES

U.S. building codes have protected us reasonably well from earthquakes and windstorms. Even though major earthquakes in the United States have resulted in dozens of deaths, similar earthquakes in areas without building codes have resulted in thousands of deaths. (Estimates of the death toll from the January 12, 2010 Haitian earthquake range from 46,000 to 316,000. This earthquake was only slightly stronger than the 1994 Northridge, CA earthquake, which resulted in about 70 deaths.) The codes may seem overly conservative until we remember this or consider the following:

- The Federal Emergency Management Agency (FEMA) estimates that on average, earthquakes cause $4.4 billion of damage annually in the United States.[4]

- The 1994 Northridge earthquake (classified only as a "strong" as opposed to a "major" or even a "great" earthquake) caused $20 billion in damage to wood-framed buildings.[5]

The building codes—IBC, *Uniform Building Code* (UBC) and *International Residential Code®* (IRC®)—provide minimum requirements for life safety. Meeting the code requirements will help save lives; exceeding the code could make the difference between a family living in a motel while its house is rebuilt after a disaster or never having to move out at all. Homeowners hardly ever complain that their houses are built too well.

1.6.1 Two main categories of building code provisions

The IBC allows you to meet the code provisions by following either prescriptive or engineered requirements. Unlicensed designers can typically design wood-framed residences less than three stories high by following the prescriptive "recipe" given in the code for conventional framing. Engineers usually follow the rules given in a completely different part of the code.

As stated in the Introduction, engineers and contractors have seemingly misunderstood the extent of each other's knowledge of shear walls for decades. A well-trained carpenter will know most of the prescriptive requirements in the code for wood frame construction but would have no reason to venture into the chapters that deal with the general structural engineering requirements. Engineered shear walls combine the requirements of both prescriptive and engineering provisions. For an engineered structural system to work properly, it must meet both sets of requirements.

Prescriptive requirements restrict design options

Because wood-framed construction has a reputation (not as well deserved as some people believe) of surviving earthquakes with little damage, the codes allow building "conventional light-framed construction" without requiring engineering. The section on conventional light-framed construction gives specific requirements for building houses (IBC Section 2308 or IRC Section R602.10.1). These prescriptive requirements include detailed requirements on construction of braced wall lines and braced wall panels, location, spacing, and percentage of bracing and what materials may be used. Where the limitations and requirements of conventional construction are not met, engineering is required. The term "braced wall" applies to conventional framing.

Some braced wall panels are restricted or not allowed in more active seismic areas. The most notable of these is let-in bracing, which cannot be used for braced wall panels for Seismic

Design Category C, D or E. (In general, this includes all of the West Coast, and parts of Idaho, Utah, Wyoming, Montana, Arkansas, Missouri, Illinois, Kentucky, Tennessee and Hawaii.) Conventional wood frame construction is not permitted at all for Seismic Design Category F. [Note that in previous codes you could look at a map to find out what "seismic (earthquake) zone" you were in. Under the IBC, the "Seismic Design Category," or SDC, is based not only on location, but also on the soil type under the building, type of construction, and other factors—so you can no longer look at a map and find out which SDC you need to design for.] Let-in bracing is not permitted in Seismic Design Categories D0, D1 and D2 under the IRC. You can still install let-in braces to stabilize your walls during construction, but that is about all they are good for. Diagonal steel-strap wall bracing is essentially the same as let-in bracing.

If you follow the rules for conventional framing, the code does not require engineering for your house. In exchange, you lose such design options as large windows near building corners, second-floor cantilevers or setbacks of more than approximately 4 feet, and split-level floor framing, to list a few. Some experts on wood-framed construction have reported that a conventionally framed house may have only one-fourth of the strength of an engineered design for the same floor plan. This occurs most notoriously in houses with high ceilings and steep roofs built in high-wind areas.[6]

The ICC publishes a complete prescriptive standard for wind-resistant design, called "Standard for Residential Construction in High-Wind Regions" (ICC 600-2008).[7] Compliance with this standard is deemed to satisfy the code requirements for high-wind-resistant construction. This reference contains many illustrations showing proper construction that apply just as well to earthquake-resistant construction. Note that compliance with AF&PA *Wood Frame Construction Manual for One- and Two-family Dwellings* (WFCM) is also permitted as an alternative to the conventional wood frame construction provisions in the IBC and IRC. The WFCM includes wind speeds up to 150 mph.

Engineered requirements allow the designer to choose how the structure will meet the code

Engineers essentially write their own prescriptive requirements for a particular building. They deal first with the code chapter that tells them, "design a building that will withstand these particular loads." Then they use provisions of chapters on foundation, concrete, masonry, steel, wood and possibly other requirements, together with engineering principles, to design the actual structure. Engineers customize each design to minimize expense while still meeting the minimum building code requirements.

In this book the term "shear wall" applies to sheathed walls that form part of an engineered system. "Braced walls" are part of a prescriptive system.

1.6.2 The two commandments of structural engineering

Section 1604.4 of the IBC states, in part: "Any system or method of construction to be used shall be based on a rational analysis in accordance with well-established principles of mechanics. Such analysis shall result in a system that provides a complete load path capable of transferring loads from their point of origin to the load-resisting elements." The implications of these two sentences are enormous.

Rational analysis

"Rational analysis" means that engineers must base each part of their designs on calculations that would make sense to any other engineer competent in that type of design. Engineers are not supposed to say things like, "I *think* this post is strong enough to keep the three stories above from collapsing on you."

Complete load path

To create a complete load path, the designer must keep track of all the loads in the structure and where they go. For lateral forces, the load path usually takes many twists and turns in a custom home. At each change in direction or offset in the load path, structural elements must somehow keep the building from ripping apart. Most people find it very hard to visualize the load path for lateral forces; this is the most challenging part of engineering most buildings.

If you follow these "commandments," your designs will better withstand the lateral forces of windstorms or earthquakes. The rest of the building code provides details on which forces you must calculate and how, and how you may use specific building materials to resist those forces.

Chapter 2

HOW SHEAR WALLS WORK

2.1

BASIC SHEAR WALL CONCEPTS

Most of us can understand wind forces more easily than the inertial forces that earthquakes generate, and for the following discussion either force has the same effect on a building. Therefore, we will talk about wind forces in the following example.

This example uses a single-story house with a flat roof, as shown in Figure 6. According to the standard the IBC uses for lateral design requirements (ASCE 7—see Reference 19), wind blowing against the face of the long wall at 90 mph exerts a horizontal pressure of about 12 pounds per square foot (psf) against the wall. (A portion of the wall near the corner of the building receives a pressure of about 14 psf). This windward wall acts like a sail. This example simplifies how wind forces really act on a house. In reality, the wind also creates suction on the roof, end walls and the back of the house, but the result is the same in that the shear walls carry the wind force to the footing, where it is resisted.

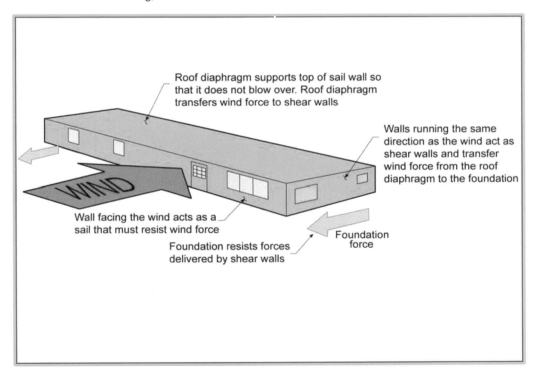

Figure 6
Wind force acting on this flat-roofed house transfers through the roof and shear walls to the footing. (For simplication, this diagram does not show suction forces that wind also causes on the roof, leeward wall and end walls.)

The windward wall would blow over if it was not supported laterally at the top. Rafters or trusses nailed to the wall top plate provide this lateral support. The roof members can resist the lateral wind force because they in turn attach to the roof sheathing, or diaphragm. The roof diaphragm acts as a deep beam laid on its side resisting the horizontal wind force. The end walls of the house provide lateral support to the ends of the diaphragm. If the roof diaphragm was not nailed to the top of the end walls, it would skid off them as the windward wall blew in.

The end walls of the house (walls running the same direction as the wind blows) function as shear walls. In this example, the shear walls are the last link in getting the wind force transferred from the windward "sail" wall to the house's footing.

Long houses usually need more than just their end walls to resist wind forces. In this case, designers call for interior shear walls to contribute to the house's stability.

The entire length of a wall typically is not designed as a shear wall. Someone usually wants some architectural feature such as a door or window placed in the wall. In this case, the only part of the wall that serves to resist horizontal forces may be between a door and a window. We will call this part of the wall a "shear wall segment."

FIVE ESSENTIAL SHEAR WALL PRINCIPLES

For a shear wall or shear wall segment to do its job, the following five features are required:

- **"Action"** Wind or earthquake forces must actually get to the shear wall .

- **"Reaction"** The shear wall must connect to the footing so that it will not slide off.

- **"Internal strength"** The shear wall must have enough strength to hold together under the earthquake or wind forces.

- **"Tie-downs"** End-posts must connect to the footing so that the wall will not tend to rock up and down, or worse, roll end over end.

- **"Bearing capacity"** End-posts must not punch through the floor platform or crush the sill or sole plate.

Figure 7 shows a schematic of these five properties working together. Figure 8 shows a shear wall and how it could fail if it did not meet the five individual requirements. The following section describes each of these five properties and how a real wood-framed shear wall meets them.

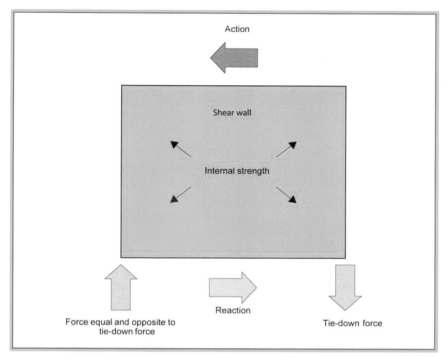

Figure 7

Forces on all four edges of a shear wall must balance each other . The wall must be strong enough to transfer those forces from each edge to the opposite edge.

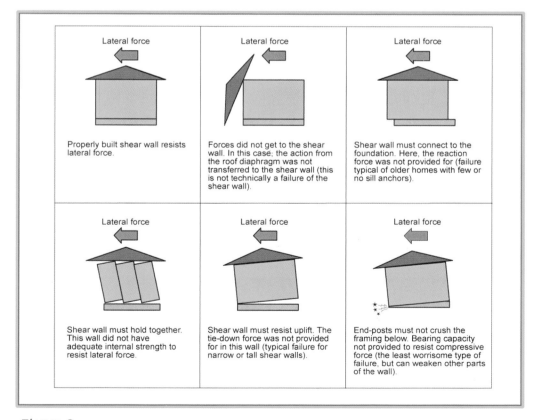

Figure 8

The above diagrams show the five basic ways that shear walls can fail. The failure modes can compound each other.

GENERIC WOOD-FRAMED SHEAR WALLS

(Beyond the Schematic Diagrams)

This section discusses the five basic ways that shear walls can fail, which fall into two main categories: things that can happen to the whole wall, no matter how strong it is (sliding off the foundation, rolling over, etc.) and the internal strength of the wall.

2.3.1 The wall as a whole

"Action"—the force that acts on the shear wall

In our example, the "action" is the wind-generated force acting at the top of the shear wall. The wind force must have a way to transfer into the shear wall from the part of the building that the wind blows against. As obvious as this sounds, one very common mistake is neglecting to even deliver the force to the shear wall.

Delivering force to a shear wall requires two general provisions: The shear wall must extend all the way up to the roof (or floor) diaphragm above, and that diaphragm must connect to the shear wall's top plate. The IBC does not explicitly require either of these conditions in the conventional framing section and nailing schedule. The code section that requires a complete load path (see "The two commandments of structural engineering" on Page 10) certainly indicates the necessity of full-height shear panels. Building plans may or may not include details that show this, depending on how much the designer assumed carpenters know about shear wall construction. Designers must show enough detail on their plans to assure that carpenters can build the shear walls properly. Carpenters following only the conventional framing requirements in the codes will not necessarily provide a complete load path.

The building codes are moving toward requiring nailing that results in a complete load path. Starting in 1994, the *Uniform Building Code* (UBC) began requiring 8-penny toenails from blocking between rafters or joists to the top plate below. (This requirement appears in Table 2304.9.1 "Fastening Schedule" in the 2009 IBC, and Table R602.3(1) "Fastener Schedule for Structural Members" in the 2009 IRC.) This accomplishes part of the load path connections from diaphragm to wall.

"Reaction"—the force that keeps the shear wall from sliding

Connections to the footing or floor platform resist the force delivered to the top of the wall. In the case of a slab floor, the sill connects to the slab with anchor bolts or other sill anchors. For a raised floor, the shear wall sole plate connects to the end or rim joist. Changes to the UBC in 1994 required nailing the sole plates of braced walls to framing below with three nails per 16 inches and nailing the rim joist to the framing or sill below with 8-penny toenails every 6 inches. These fastening requirements were incorporated into the IBC to help assure that the wind or earthquake forces are transferred all the way to the footing.

"Tie-downs"—forces that keep the shear wall from rolling over

Building sturdy shear walls is not always enough. If we just leave the action and reaction forces described above to themselves, the shear wall segments will tend to roll over. Engineers call this "overturning." In some cases, the weight of the shear wall and the structure above it will keep it from rolling over, but most shear walls need additional overturning resistance. In this case you must install "tie-downs" at each end of the shear wall segment to connect it to the footing. (Only one tie-down will function at a time, as described in the next section.)

Manufacturers such as KC Metals, Simpson, USP, and Zone Four make a wide variety of tie-down hardware. Figure 9 shows several examples of tie-downs. The simplest of these are steel straps that you cast into the footing concrete at both ends of each shear wall segment. Part of the strap extends out of the concrete. You then nail the extending strap securely to the end stud or post in the shear wall segment. For larger overturning forces, the tie-downs may be welded or formed steel that bolt, nail or screw to the end studs of the shear wall and also connect to an anchor rod cast into the footing.

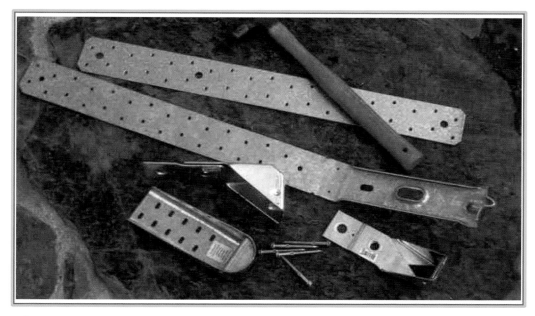

Figure 9

Example of several types of tie-downs. The bottom three brackets attach to anchor rods cast into the concrete footing and then to wood framing (with bolts or the special wood screws shown); the long strap in the middle is cast into the concrete and then nailed onto the framing; the strap shown at the top (under the hammer) could tie across floor levels, although longer straps would do better.

Note that ordinary sill anchors do not help keep the wall from lifting up off the foundation. There are a number of reasons for this. First, the sills can easily rip up over nuts and washers on anchor bolts (especially when holes for the anchor bolts are oversized). Second, for the sill to transfer forces from the shear panels to the anchor bolts, the wood must resist "cross-grain bending." Cross-grain bending is the very weakest property of wood; when you grasp the edges of a wood shingle, you can easily bend and snap it lengthwise by taking advantage of this weakness. Figure 10 shows a shear wall where the mudsill failed in cross-grain bending. Third, the nails along the bottom of the shear panels could easily tear out of the panel edges. Fourth, the sill attaches to the wrong edge of the shear wall to transfer vertical forces into the wall.

Figure 10
The mudsill in this shear wall test failed in cross-grain bending, causing it to split lengthwise. This can occur if uplift is resisted only by mudsill anchors and not tie-downs.
(Photo courtesy of Rob Y. H. Chai, CUREE-Caltech Woodframe Project).

"Bearing capacity" of platform or sill supporting shear wall end-posts

People often overlook the opposite effect of overturning. A downward force occurs at the same time, but at the opposite end of the shear wall from the uplift force. Note that both ends of the shear wall must have bearing capacity under the end-posts and the ability to resist uplift because the "action" force on the wall could come from either direction.

The properties of wood can cause problems in shear wall construction. Trees make wood with one main intention: to support their own weight. Therefore wood is very strong in the direction of the wood grain. However, wood crushes easily across the grain. When you place a post on the sole plate of a wall, in most cases the end of the post will crush the side grain of the plate long before the post itself becomes overloaded.

You must provide solid support under the ends of shear walls in addition to providing for tie-down forces. Sometimes this means using end-posts that seem oversized (so they will not crush the sill) or putting the posts in steel post bases that bear directly on the concrete slab or footing.

2.3.2 Combined external forces on a shear wall

Each external force acting on the wall is transferred through an element along the full width or height of the wall, parallel to the wall edge. The top plate transfers the action force into the wall, the sill (or sole plate if the wall is built on a raised floor) transfers force from the wall to the structure below, and the end-posts transmit vertical forces to the foundation to keep the wall from overturning.

The wall illustrated may appear as a rigid element that will not deform under loads. This assumption can lead to some improper conclusions about how the wall resists forces. For example, it may seem that the sill anchors will provide resistance to overturning. The sill anchors very effectively keep the wall from sliding, but they cannot resist much uplift at all. Think of how you tear a sheet of paper out of a spiral-bound notebook—that is the same action that would rip the sheathing away from the sill, or lift the sill over the anchor bolts, one nail or bolt at a time. The wall will deform under loads (the nature of these deformations is beyond the scope of this book), but if we construct it correctly it will not come apart or move from where we built it.

2.3.3 Internal strength of the shear wall

The previous section discussed the four ways that a shear wall could fail even if it was made of titanium alloy. We will now discuss the fifth essential property of a shear wall—its internal strength.

Properly built shear walls use materials that are fairly flimsy by themselves. To make a sturdy structural element, we must connect all the pieces of the wall so that they act together. This section discusses how to connect all the components of a shear wall so that it will serve its purpose.

Figure 11 shows four arrows representing action, reaction, and the tie-down and bearing forces. We have not yet discussed how these forces transfer through the wall to meet and cancel each other. For this we introduce what engineers call a "shear element," the plywood or OSB sheathing that covers the wall and gives it the term "shear" wall. A shear element is, in theory, a very small square of material that has forces acting parallel to each of its edges. The four forces on such a square are all equal. Forces along the top and bottom of the square act in opposite directions, and the force on one side acts upward while the force on the other side acts downward. The direction of the side forces must also oppose the tendency for the square to rotate due to the top and bottom forces. In other words, if the top and bottom forces act to rotate the square clockwise, the side forces must act counter-clockwise. Figure 12 shows a shear element taken from the upper right corner of the wall.

The simplest shear wall would have a single piece of sheathing covering the whole wall. This sheathing would have nails along the top, bottom and both sides at, say, 6-inch spacing. Figure 12 shows how each nail along the edge of the sheathing panel exerts a small force on the panel. Most people can easily see how the forces transfer through the panel and meet the opposing forces from the far panel edge.

So what happens in the almost universal case that our wall is bigger than a single piece of sheathing? This part becomes a little less intuitive. Because we have established that the wall must not move, and because of the way leverage works, it turns out that each nail around the perimeter of each piece of sheathing exerts the same force. (This is basic theory. Laboratory tests show that nails near panel corners take more force and in different directions than nails near the midpoint of each edge.) The height or length of the wall does not matter. If you install nails at the same spacing along all four edges of the sheathing panels, you will have the exact number of nails needed along each particular edge to transfer the action, reaction and overturning forces into the panel. Our shear element has the same amount of force for each foot along each of its edges, whether the top or bottom edge or either side. It turns out that we can divide the single panel into as many imaginary (or real) pieces as we want, and each piece will have the same force along each foot of the edge. (This holds true only for pieces with horizontal and vertical edges, which covers typical installation of sheathing.)

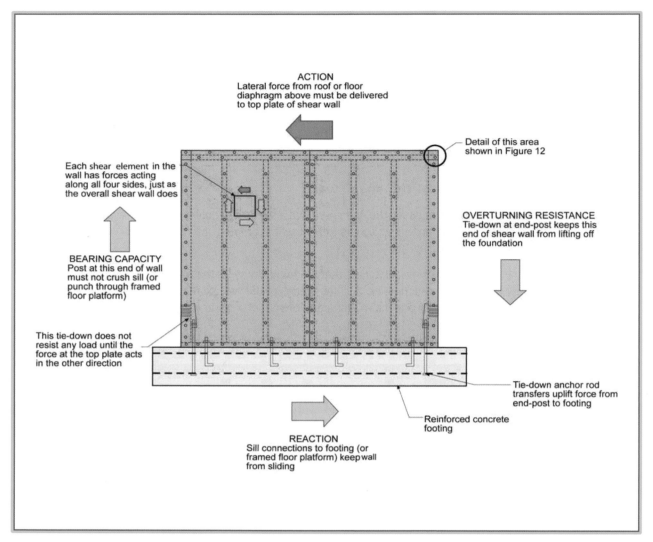

ACTION
Lateral force from roof or floor diaphragm above must be delivered to top plate of shear wall

Detail of this area shown in Figure 12

Each shear element in the wall has forces acting along all four sides, just as the overall shear wall does

OVERTURNING RESISTANCE
Tie-down at end-post keeps this end of shear wall from lifting off the foundation

BEARING CAPACITY
Post at this end of wall must not crush sill (or punch through framed floor platform)

This tie-down does not resist any load until the force at the top plate acts in the other direction

Tie-down anchor rod transfers uplift force from end-post to footing

Reinforced concrete footing

REACTION
Sill connections to footing (or framed floor platform) keep wall from sliding

Figure 11

The four arrows in the diagram above show the forces that must act on a shear wall for it to work as intended. Shear panels nailed to the wall framing transfer forces from the top to the bottom and from one side of the wall to the other. These forces are transferred in line with each particular framing member. Because of this, the sill cannot transfer enough vertical force into the shear wall to resist overturning.

The transfer of forces from one side of the wall to the other may become more intuitive if you think of a square of sheathing somewhere in the panel, as highlighted in Figure 11. For this square of sheathing to remain in the same place, the forces on it must cancel each other.

The shear forces acting on the top and bottom edges of the square are equal and opposite in direction, as are the forces on the left and right sides. If this square were at a corner of the shear wall, as shown in Figure 12, then the forces would be applied by the nails along the top and right edges and through the sheathing material itself on the bottom and left edges.

We can build a shear wall of any size out of sheathing panels that meet over common framing members, as long as we nail all the edges of each panel uniformly. Vertical panel joints must occur over studs and horizontal joints over rows of blocking. The joints must not allow panels to slip past each other, or the wall will deform. The old water tower shown in Figure 13 has shifted because the boards slipped past one another along the vertical joints. This wall was constructed of 1 x 12-inch boards, but the same thing can happen to 4 by 8-foot panels without proper edge nailing. A building with horizontal siding could deform similarly. Either case gives you a diamond-shaped wall.

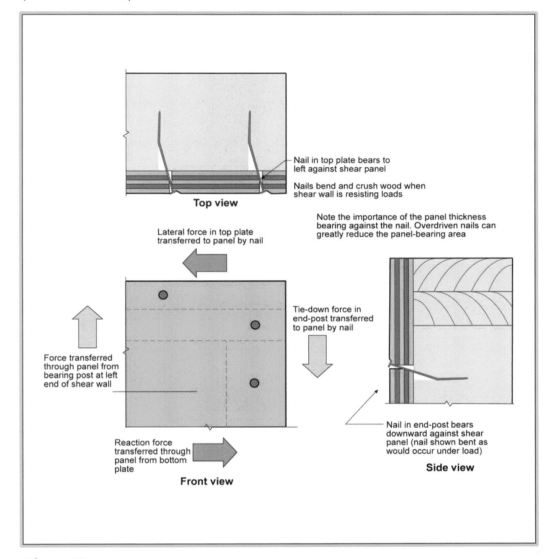

Figure 12

Detail of top right corner of shear wall shown in Figure 11. Top and side views show how each nail bears against the shear panel and transfers a small amount of force to the panel from the wall top plate or the shear wall end-post.

Figure 13
This building twisted as the joints between the siding boards slipped, racking the walls.

LABORATORY TESTS OF SHEAR WALLS

2.4.1 Test procedures

APA–The Engineered Wood Association has tested plywood and OSB shear walls extensively, beginning in the 1950s. Most of the walls tested were 8-feet wide by 8-feet tall. Code development committees used the results of these tests to determine the allowable strengths given in the model building codes for various panel thicknesses and nailing schedules. These first tests were "monotonic," meaning that the base of the wall was held in a rigid jig while a sideways load was applied from one direction at the top of the wall, in line with the wall's top-plate. They increased the load until the wall deformed so much that it began to come apart and lose its strength.[8]

Earthquakes test real shear walls with loads applied violently back and forth. This action has a much more severe effect on a shear wall than just pushing it in one direction. After the 1989 Loma Prieta, CA earthquake damaged shear wall structures more severely than expected, engineers took a hard look at the test procedures and allowable design values in the codes. After the 1994 Northridge earthquake, the city of Los Angeles even reduced all the allowable shear wall values given in the UBC by 25 percent.

Most engineers agree that shear wall tests should use loads applied cyclically, or back and forth, to more realistically imitate earthquakes. Exactly how to apply this cyclic loading will probably remain under debate for quite some time. In the mid 1990s APA tested some shear walls under cyclic loading.[9] The test results for both monotonic and cyclic tests are summarized below.

2.4.2 How shear walls failed during testing

Both test methods (monotonic and cyclic) produced one or more of the following failures:

- The nails bent due to the lateral bearing of the shear panels against them, and their heads tore through the panels (internal strength failure).

- The end-posts crushed the bottom wall plates, which resulted in excessive deflection and made the former problem worse (bearing capacity failure).

- Nails placed too close to panel edges tore out of the panel (internal strength failure).

- Where nails (especially 10-penny common) were closely spaced, the studs split (internal strength failure).

For tests done under cyclic loading, nails also failed in fatigue as they were bent back and forth repeatedly and snapped off about $3/8$-inch below the face of the stud or got worked out of the studs by the back-and-forth action of the panels against them (internal strength failure).

The tests that formed the basis for the building code strength tables used shear walls built in laboratories by people who knew exactly how to build them. Therefore, the action force always got to the walls (otherwise the tests would have been very boring). All nails, blocking and tie-down hardware were also installed properly. Photos of walls in one test show nails carefully installed along chalklines snapped on the framing members. If you build a shear wall in real life, you may encounter difficulties that do not occur in a laboratory—for example, misplaced sill anchors, split and twisted lumber, supervisors who belittle the need for a chalkline, etc.

2.4.3 Considerations for future testing

Researchers certainly should use cyclic loading to get realistic strength values for shear walls. They also should use realistic shear walls for their tests. Although it is unrealistic to try to guess all the ways that a shear wall might be improperly built and duplicate those conditions in tests, certain factors seem obvious.

Use the same materials commonly found on construction sites

Formal research accepted by the codes typically was based on the use of common or galvanized box nails. These might have been readily available 50 years ago, but that is no longer the case. Reliable but anonymous sources report that prominent researchers had to special order common nails to assemble sample shear walls for recent tests. This should send a message to the engineering and testing community.

Follow typical construction procedures

Besides using truly common materials, researchers should build test walls to the same dimensions used in construction. Research reports I studied while preparing this guide repeatedly referred to 8-foot, 0-inch by 8-foot, 0-inch test panels. This was convenient for attaching two full sheets of shear panels to framing. However, typical framed walls are taller than 8-feet, 0-inch. On the west coast, most walls are 8 foot, $3/4$-inch tall, which allows for ceiling drywall installation. On the east coast, most builders add 1x strapping to the underside of ceiling framing. This means they frame their walls even taller. Where does this leave an 8-foot shear panel? Floating somewhere above the bottom edge of the sill or sole plate, or below the top of the double plate, or both. Will this make a big difference in a shear wall's performance? It certainly would if you do not have enough room to nail along the top or bottom panel edge without splitting it.

2.5

EXAMPLE—SHEAR WALL ON A SLAB FOOTING, WITH REAL NUMBERS

Now that we have some background on how shear walls work, let's take a look at a simple shear wall and find out what various forces act on it.

Figure 14 shows a simple shear wall, 12-feet long and 8-feet tall with a 3,600-pound force applied to the top. We immediately know that a reaction force of 3,600 pounds must act in the opposite direction at the bottom of the wall.

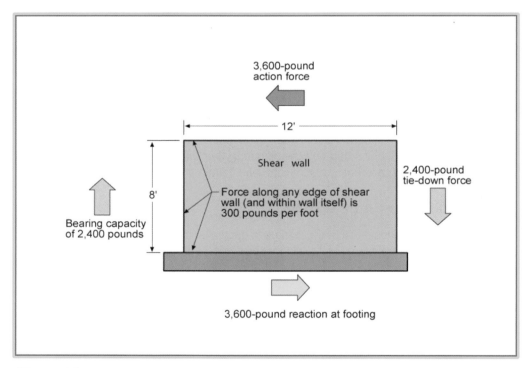

Figure 14
Example of shear wall loading and resulting forces.

Next we can determine the unit shear stress in the wall sheathing. If we divide 3,600 pounds by the length of the wall, we find that every foot of wall must resist 300 pounds (3,600 pounds/12 feet = 300 pounds/foot).

That takes care of the action and reaction; now we must address overturning. There are two ways to find out what the upward and downward forces are at each end of the wall. The first method goes back to what we established earlier—that the force along each foot of a vertical

3.1.3 Construction problems can compound each other

The following sections list many building requirements. Meeting all that apply to your project should give you the "perfect shear wall." But ignoring some of them could mean that errors will work together to make your shear wall *much* less effective than the designer intended.

As an example, let's say that our plans call for $3/_8$-inch sheathing with edge nailing at 4 inches to 2x studs using 8-penny common nails driven into Douglas Fir framing. What is built in the field uses 8-penny "cooler" nails (0.113-inch diameter, $2^3/_8$ inches long). Instead of Douglas Fir the sill is Hem-Fir, which is more commonly available than Douglas Fir as pressure-treated material (Hem-Fir accepts chemical treatment more easily than Douglas Fir).

The original design was based on a shear wall capacity of 350 pounds per foot (see the left-hand column for a "Type 4" wall in the Sample Shear Wall Schedule on Page 31). The deviations from the plans have the following effects:

Cooler nails at 4 inches in $3/_8$-inch sheathing have an allowable capacity of 245 pounds per foot (given in ICC Evaluation Service Report 1539[10], [ESR-1539], Table 17).

Hem-Fir lumber is not as dense as Douglas Fir. Nails in Hem-Fir give only 82 percent of the connection strength of nails in Douglas Fir (Footnote a in IBC Table 2306.3., the table that gives allowable shear wall capacities).

Now our wall strength is 245 pounds per foot multiplied by 82 percent, or (245 pounds per foot) x 0.82 = 201 pounds per foot.

We have reduced our wall strength from 350 pounds per foot to 201 pounds per foot. *Our wall has lost over forty percent of its intended strength!* What if we also had overdriven nails, thinner sheathing or nails spaced farther apart than specified on the plans? Field inspectors commonly find two or more such problems in the same shear wall.

Most of the above items will be discussed in more detail under the section titled, "Internal Strength—Making the Wall Strong Enough to Resist the Load" beginning on Page 48.

3.1.4 Special inspection of shear walls and related elements

The IBC now requires periodic special inspection for construction in high wind or earthquake classifications (IBC Sections 1706 and 1707). For wind, the requirements apply in Wind Exposure Category B where the 3-second gust basic wind speed is 120 mph or greater, or in Wind Exposure C or D where the 3-second gust basic wind speed is 110 mph or greater. For seismic the requirement applies to all construction for Seismic Design Categories C, D, E, or F. These wind and earthquake classifications cover virtually all of the west coast of the U.S., the Gulf Coast, and much of the east coast.

Special inspection requirements apply to "nailing, bolting, anchoring and other fastening of components within the main windforce- or seismic-force-resisting system, including wood shear walls, wood diaphragms, drag struts, braces, shear panels, and hold-downs" (IBC Sections 1706.2 and 1707.3)

A partial exception to this requirement applies if the sheathing nailing is spaced more than 4 inches apart and states that special inspection is not required for "wood shear walls, shear panels and diaphragms, including nailing, bolting, anchoring and other fastening to other components of the windforce- or seismic-force-resisting system". Whether *all* the special inspection requirements are excluded is not entirely clear. Do drag struts, braces, and hold-downs still require special inspection? There is some opportunity for local jurisdictions to interpret these requirements.

Designers should be aware of the above requirements and the exception to them, which leaves 6-inch edge nailing as the only option to eliminate special inspection costs. Designing with only this lighter nailing schedule limits the strength of shear walls considerably. Contemporary building designs often dictate the use of shear panel nailing at spacings much less than 6 inches.

3.1.5 Sample shear wall schedule

Your plans may include a shear wall schedule that calls out information such as sill anchor size and spacing, stud sizes, end-post sizes, tie-downs, framing connectors to fasten to framing below, shear panel thickness, nail size and spacing and other information relevant to the design. Note that shear wall schedules vary from one designer to another. A "Type 1" shear wall on one set of plans may be the same as a "Type 8" designated by another designer or a "Type E" by another.

The APA's initial research listed strength values for five panel thicknesses, three sizes of nails and four edge-nailing spacings. Their table lists 48 different combinations for all these variables. The International Staple, Nail and Tool Association (ISANTA) had engineers calculate the theoretical strength of many different sized fasteners based on the 1991 *National Design Specification for Wood Construction.* These calculations are the basis for legacy National Evaluation Service Report 272 (NER-272), which has been replaced by ICC Evaluation Service Report 1539[10] (ESR-1539), which the model building codes accept as the allowable strengths for these fasteners. The results of these calculations make up approximately eight pages of tables and 540 entries for shear walls alone. Designers choose the panel thickness and nailing requirements from this huge selection to meet the needs of their projects. To make things even more complicated, the Special Design Provisions for Wind and Seismic[18] (introduced with the 2009 IBC) give allowable shear values depending on whether the forces on the wall are generated by wind or earthquakes (strength values may be increased by 40 percent to resist wind forces). Furthermore, these values are adjusted according to whether the designer is using "allowable stress design" or "load and resistance factor design". A sample shear wall schedule is shown on the following pages with some notes regarding shear wall construction. The shear values listed in the schedule depend on strict adherence to all of the Shear Wall Notes.

SAMPLE SHEAR WALL SCHEDULE (See Note 1)

MAX. SHEAR* (lbs./ft.)	SYMBOL ON PLAN	SILL ANCHOR BOLTS (2, 4, 7, 8, 19)	MINIMUM SILL THICKNESS (3)	TIE-DOWN ANCHOR ROD (4, 5, 6)	MINIMUM END-POST (4)	TIE-DOWNS (4, 5)	SHEATHING (Plywood or OSB) (9, 10, 12, 13)	PANEL EDGE NAILING (14, 15, 16, 17, 18)
180	△1	$1/2''$ @ 6' (18)	2x	N/A	Dbl. 2x	(Designer must select tie-downs from locally available mfrs. or distributors)	$5/16''$ (11)	6d @ 6"
200	△2	$5/8''$ @ 6'	2x	N/A	Dbl. 2x		$3/8''$ (11)	6d @ 6"
260	△3	$5/8''$ @ 6'	2x	$5/8'' \times 15''$	Dbl. 2x		$3/8''$ (11)	8d @ 6"
350**	△4	$5/8''$ @ 4'	2x	$5/8'' \times 15''$	Dbl. 2x		$3/8''$ (11)	8d @ 4"

SEE NOTE 3 (on the next page)

MAX. SHEAR* (lbs./ft.)	SYMBOL ON PLAN	SILL ANCHOR BOLTS (2, 4, 7, 8, 19)	MINIMUM SILL THICKNESS (3)	TIE-DOWN ANCHOR ROD (4, 5, 6)	MINIMUM END-POST (4)	TIE-DOWNS (4, 5)	SHEATHING (Plywood or OSB) (9, 10, 12, 13)	PANEL EDGE NAILING (14, 15, 16, 17, 18)
490	△5	$5/8''$ @ 4'	3x	$5/8'' \times 15''$	4x		$3/8''$ (11)	8d @ 3"
600	△6	$5/8''$ @ 3'-4"	3x	$5/8'' \times 18''$	4x		$15/32''$	10d @ 3"
770	△7	$5/8''$ @ 2'-6"	3x	$7/8'' \times 18''$	4x		$15/32''$	10d @ 2"
870	△8	$5/8''$ @ 2'-3"	3x	$7/8'' \times 18''$	4x		$19/32''$ or $15/32''$ Structural 1	10d @ 2"

* Maximum shear is shown here for reference only. Values in the Shear Wall Schedule are based on Table 2306.3 from the 2009 IBC. Values listed above may be increased by 40% for wind loading per IBC Section 2306.3 *These values are subject to revision.* The IBC tables are based on testing done by APA—The Engineered Wood Association.

** 380 if 3x framing is used under all panel joints.

SAMPLE SHEAR WALL NOTES

1. The shear wall schedule is based on single-story construction with 8-foot-high walls; for two-story construction or different wall heights, see plans for end-post and tie-down sizes.

2. Use standard anchor bolts: minimum 10 inches for 2x plates, minimum 12 inches for 3x or 4x plates.

3. Use **BORATE-TREATED** lumber for mudsills, not ACQ, CA, CC or ACZA.

4. Walls shown in the shaded area of the shear wall schedule require minimum 3x lumber for sills at footings and for studs at shear panel joints. Use longer sill anchor bolts as needed.

5. For walls with sheathing on both sides, space sill anchor bolts at one-half of the table spacing. These walls will require larger tie-downs and end-posts (see foundation plan).

6. Tie-downs are required at both ends of each section of shear wall as shown on the plans, unless specifically shown otherwise.

7. All-thread rod of the given diameter, with a double nut at the bottom, may be used as tie-down anchor rods.

8. For Seismic Design Category D, E and F, use 3-inch-square, 0.229-inch-thick plate washers at all sill anchor bolts in shear walls (available through several connector hardware manufacturers).

9. Fill any oversized holes in sills at anchor bolts with "Pour-Stone" or equal non-shrink grout, or epoxy.

10. Plywood and OSB are interchangeable for interior walls only. For exterior shear walls, use plywood. For shear panels thicker than $^{3}/_{8}$-inch, use 5-ply plywood. Type 303 plywood siding ("T1-11," shiplap, reverse board-and-batten, etc.) may be used for shear walls. The effective sheathing thickness is the plywood thickness that the nails are driven through. *For shiplap and reverse board and batten siding, use 4x studs under all panel joints in shear walls*.

11. Attach shear panels directly to studs. Where required for fire resistive construction, install gypsum board over shear panels, increasing the required minimum gypsum board fastener length by the shear panel thickness.

12. Install $^{7}/_{16}$-inch or thinner sheathing with long dimension of sheets oriented horizontally if studs are spaced more than 16 inches apart.

13. Install blocking behind all horizontal panel joints. Flat 2x blocking may be used for 8-penny or smaller nails; use minimum 3x blocking for 10-penny nails.

14. Holes in shear panels for electrical outlets, switches, etc., shall be neatly cut, with rounded corners. (Use a saber saw or a Sawzall, not a Skilsaw!) Maximum hole size is 6-inch diameter.

15. *For fastening shear panels, air-driven "plywood nails" are preferred.* For 8-penny nails, use 0.131 inch diameter x 2 inch long nails; for 10-penny, use 0.148 inch diameter x 2-$^{1}/_{8}$ inch long nails. *Gun nails shall have full round heads*. For hand-driven nails, use *common* or *galvanized box* nails..

16. Drive nail heads flush with the outer sheathing layer; inspector may require that panels with nails driven so as to damage the outer sheathing layer be replaced. Use special care when using pneumatic nail guns. Nails with oversized heads are recommended.

17. Edge nailing spacing is at all edges of all panels in the shear wall as designated on the plans, except as in Note 18 below.

18. Edge nailing at ends of shear walls is to post with tie-down attached to it, even if sheathing extends past the post.

19. For Seismic Design Category E or F, minimum anchor bolt diameter is $^{5}/_{8}$- inch

More Shear Wall Notes

- The above Sample Shear Wall Schedule and Notes reflect the minimum requirements that I feel are appropriate for shear wall construction. In a couple of instances these notes go beyond the minimum code requirements.

- Shear wall strength values shown are for earthquake forces; for shear walls resisting wind forces, listed values may be increased by 40 percent.

- Engineers who study earthquake damage generally agree that five-ply plywood at least $^{15}/_{32}$" thick performs much better than thinner panels or four-ply, three-layer plywood.

- In reality, I only specify Types 3, 4, 6 and 8 shear walls. The only difference between Types 5 and 6 walls is the nail size. Using 10-penny nails instead of 8-pennies will give you a much stronger shear wall for almost no added expense. Likewise, using $^{19}/_{32}$" or Structural I plywood to go from a Type 7 to Type 8 wall adds little cost compared to the benefit.

ACTION—GETTING THE LOADS INTO THE SHEAR WALL

3.2.1 Sheath all the way to the roof at gable ends

For single-story houses, you must extend the sheathing from the bottom of the shear wall all the way up to the roof framing. You must sheath the entire area of gable end walls. Along eave walls, frieze blocking typically connects the roof sheathing to the shear wall top plate. The Standard for Residential Construction in High Wind Regions calls for this and provides illustrations of proper installation.

Figure 16 shows a gable end wall that will never "feel" the forces it was designed for because the shear wall panels stop at the sloped top plate of the end wall. This problem appears in almost every new housing tract I see throughout California. Some builders do get it right though; Figure 17 shows a house built one block away that does have the necessary connection from the roof diaphragm to the shear wall.

3.2.2 Extend interior shear walls up to the roof sheathing

Interior walls are used for shear walls more frequently now to help make up for large expanses of windows in the exterior walls of contemporary homes. In standard wood-framed construction, interior walls do not extend higher than the ceiling level. For such walls you have at best a double-plate lap at both ends of the wall with two 16-penny nails to the exterior wall plates (which are indirectly connected to the roof diaphragm through rafters or trusses). These four nails could resist about 500 pounds of lateral force. At worst you have no connections if neither end of your interior wall butts against an outside wall. For a shear wall that may need to resist several thousand pounds, not providing a path for this force to be transferred to the wall is a very serious—and unfortunately very common—mistake.

Figure 18 shows a wall that someone expected to carry significant force—note all the shiny metal framing connectors fastening the truss bottom chord to the wall top plate—but there is no positive connection between the shear wall and the roof sheathing. Without any diagonal members, this truss cannot transfer lateral forces from the roof diaphragm to the top plate. (It should be emphasized that trusses are not typically designed to transfer such forces; the best practice is to extend the wall all the way up to the underside of the sheathing.) Figure 19 shows a properly built shear wall sheathed up to the underside of the roof diaphragm. Again, the Standard for Residential Construction in High Wind Regions calls for and illustrates such connections.

Figure 16
BAD—Forces in the roof diaphragm sheathing have no way to transfer to this shear wall sheathing.

Figure 17
GOOD—This shear wall connects to the roof diaphragm, as it should.

Figure 18
BAD—This interior shear wall should extend to the underside of the roof.

Figure 19
GOOD—This wall will resist lateral loads as intended.

Extending shear panels to the roof becomes more difficult when the trusses run perpendicular to the shear wall. Figure 20 shows a wall that stops about 6 feet short of where it should. Figure 21 shows infill shear frames (faced with OSB on the near side) above a shear wall. The roof sheathing must be nailed to the top members of every frame. Notice the gaps where the truss members pass between these frames; the only way to connect the shear frames together is by nailing to the truss web members. Each frame acts as a shear element that transfers force from the roof sheathing above to the wall top plate. Shear elements must have forces acting along each edge, and air gaps cannot provide these forces. Figure 22 shows infill shear frames nailed to a truss with no gaps, ready for roof sheathing to be installed and nailed along the tops of the frames.

Figure 20
BAD—Shear walls need to extend up through framing.

Figure 21
A GOOD START—These shear frames between trusses must rely on proper connections to the trusses.

Figure 22
GOOD—These shear frames will have connections on all four sides.

Designers should realize that adding shear frames or truss frames above a shear walll will turn this wall into a bearing wall; the added framing will support the trusses at that point. Trusses and footings must be designed accordingly.

Figure 23 shows a full-height shear wall that the trusses hang from—the best practice in this situation. Breaking the trusses at a full-height shear wall also eliminates considerable labor installing shear frames.

The plans should include details for all of the cases described above.

3.2.3 In multistory buildings, connect floor diaphragms to interior shear walls below

When you build a shear wall under a framed floor, the forces must have a way to transfer from the floor diaphragm to the shear paneling. Figure 24 shows a shear wall with nothing but ducts, piping and air to transfer lateral forces to it from the floor sheathing above.

Figure 25 shows a better installation with blocks between the joists above the wall. As noted in the previous section, the blocks need to act as shear elements. Nailing from the floor sheathing into the blocks transfers force to each block; the sheet metal framing connector transfers the force to the shear wall top plate. However, only bearing against the I-joist flanges will prevent these blocks from rotating. Granted, it would take considerable force to make these blocks rotate, but installing web stiffeners at the joists and toe-nailing the blocks to the stiffeners assures optimum performance.

Figure 26 shows "truss frames," an alternative to shear frames between floor trusses. (These could be used just as effectively between roof trusses.) Such truss frames must be designed for lateral forces specified by the design professional; the diagonal member must be connected adequately to carry considerable tension and compression. Just as with blocks, the frames must have connections along all four edges.

Again, the plans should include details for all of these connections.

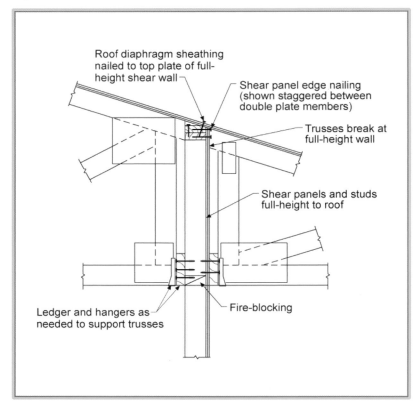

Figure 23
Full-height shear wall with trusses supported on both sides.

3.2.4 Nail the roof or floor sheathing to the blocks above the shear walls

Generally each edge, or "boundary" in engineering terms, of a roof or floor diaphragm must connect to a shear wall below. Boundary nailing provides this connection. Boundary nailing at the eave walls consists of nails from the roof sheathing into the eave (frieze) blocks. (Nailing to an overhanging fascia board does nothing to transfer forces from the roof to the wall below.) For an engineered shear wall, you must nail the sheathing to the eave blocks.

Roof sheathing nailing to the eave blocking is not specifically noted in the prescriptive nailing schedules of the code. Some background on the code nailing requirements indicates that the code is headed in the direction of closing this gap in the load path. In 1994, the *Uniform Building Code* was updated to require that blocking between joists or rafters gets toe-nailed to the plate below with three 8-penny nails per block. Another 1994 UBC update required the same nailing from rim joists or rafters to the plate below. Requirements for nailing roof sheathing to eave blocking should appear in future versions of the code. Some building inspectors require this nailing despite the fact that it's not explicitly required in the current code. Even if this goes beyond the current requirements of the nailing schedule, it helps form a complete lateral load path. However, for an engineered lateral design, the boundary nailing at the eave should be included in the structural details.

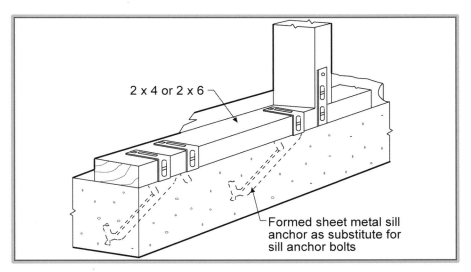

2 x 4 or 2 x 6

Formed sheet metal sill
anchor as substitute for
sill anchor bolts

Figure 28
This sill anchor solves some of the problems of conventional anchor bolts but may introduce others.

3.3.9 Use 3x sills when needed

For heavily loaded shear walls, the designer may have required 3x sills. If you have already framed your walls with 2x sills, only to find that 3x stock was required, you may still salvage the situation. You may be able to meet the design requirements by adding expansion or adhesive anchors to the sill. Clearly, you will need to confer with the building designer in such a case. (Note: Previous codes required 3x mudsills for shear walls above certain strength levels; this requirement was dropped from the 2009 IBC. I still recommend using 3x sill stock for shear walls with 8-penny nails spaced at 3 inches or less, or 10-penny nails spaced at 4 inches or less. Shear panels are usually installed above the bottom of the mudsill—especially on slab footings, to elevate them from the concrete—and a 3x sill will greatly increase the sill area that you can nail into at the bottom of the shear wall.)

Figure 29 shows a 3x sill with many anchor bolts (bent and leaning studs were not required by the engineer).

You also may want to use 2x sills instead of 3x to keep all of your stud lengths the same. Otherwise you might use standard-length studs on a 2x sill and then get to a shear wall segment that calls for a 3x sill. Now you have to cut all the shear wall studs shorter. You may want to deal with a few more sill anchor bolts rather than trim a few studs. Again, the designer will need to approve this change.

3.3.10 Install enough sill anchors

Check the plans carefully. The designer should indicate on the plans if shear walls or shear wall segments need more sill anchors than are provided by the maximum spacing otherwise allowed by the code. Designers should include this information on the foundation plan. Figure 30 shows a 2x sill with relatively close anchor spacing.

When in doubt, use more sill anchors than required. During pre-pour foundation observation visits I have never told a contractor to take anchors out, but I have required them to add anchors. You do not want to be doing this as the concrete truck is backing up to your footing forms!

Figure 29
This 3x sill will provide extra room for nailing. Nailing to the leaning studs will be a challenge.

Figure 30
This shear wall needed anchor bolts spaced much more closely than the maximum otherwise allowed by code. Note the 4x4 and 4x6 posts under shear-panel joints.

3.3.11 Provide adequate sole-plate connections to framed-floor platforms

For decades the UBC Nailing Schedule called for 16-penny nails spaced at 16 inches from the sole plate to the framing below. A revision to the UBC in 1994, which was incorporated into the IBC, requires three 16-penny nails per 16 inches from the sole plate to joists or blocking below at braced wall panels. Prescriptive braced wall panels are not the same as engineered shear walls, and serious shear walls will require many more connectors than this. Check your plans and the shear wall schedule. You may need to use lag screws or even machine bolts from the sole plate to the framing below. The framing below could include blocking between joists over a shear wall below, a rim joist, shear wall top plate, collector (see Section 4.3) or other members.

Various framing connectors and construction techniques offer options to cumbersome lags or bolts. A good, complete shear wall schedule with accompanying details will show these connections. Figure 31 shows a sole plate with increased nailing to the floor framing (there is a 4 x 12 beam below this wall). Figure 32 shows a second-floor shear wall connected to the framing below with lag screws every 8 inches, in accordance with the note inside the triangle spray-painted on the subfloor. Note the 4 x 4 sole plate used. Proprietary self-drilling screws such as Simpsons "SDS" screw series or USP's "WS" series could also make this connection.

Figure 31
Extra nailing transfers forces from this shear wall sole plate to a 4 x 12 beam in the floor framing below.

3.3.12 Connect floor platforms to framing below

The code nailing schedules require toe-nailing rim joists and blocking to framing below with 8-penny nails at 6-inch spacing. You would toe-nail to the top plate of a cripple wall or a full-height wall below, or to the sill installed on top of a footing stemwall. Toe-nailing rim joists to the framing below may be adequate; however, for heavier shear walls you will need to install framing connectors across this joint. (The IBC restricts the allowable load for toenails to 150 pounds per foot for Seismic Design Categories D, E and F. See Section 4.1.7 of SDPWS-08 for specifics.) Again, the designer should note this on the plans. Framing connectors must fasten directly to the main framing members. The connectors shown in Figure 33 with shims between them and the I-joist flange will not perform as intended. Using a single, long spacer nailed adequately to the rim joist would work better. (Figure 33 shows an I-joist used as a rim board. Although the manufacturer states that this use is suitable, most engineers would recommend using a solid rim board.) Figure 34 shows a row of properly installed connectors that fasten directly to the rim joist and the wall top plate. Contractors note that toe-nailing tends to split engineered lumber rim boards more easily than sawn lumber.

Figure 32
Lag bolts connect this 4 x 4 plate to the framing below.

3.3.13 Alternative detailing can reduce how many connections you need

If you nail your shear panels directly to the rim joist, you do not need to worry about connections from sole plate to rim joist or rim joist to the plate below. Your designer would have to provide details for this alternative. This would require lapping shear panels onto the rim joist. If you use engineered lumber for the platform framing, you typically may also have to use a rim board thicker than the standard $1\frac{1}{4}$-inch stock. For shear walls nailed with 10-penny nails, you need to use rim board stock that is at least $1\frac{1}{2}$ inches thick for sufficient embedment of the nails into the rim board.

Figure 33
BAD—These framing connectors installed on spacers will not perform well.
Bending the connectors over onto the I-joist flange and omitting the spacers
would have been better.

Figure 34
GOOD—The row of connectors will transfer loads as intended from the second-floor rim joist to
the wall top plate below.

3.3.14 Above and beyond the code

The following suggestions can add significant strength to your shear walls. Some items take almost no effort; others will only appeal to seismically paranoid builders.

- Engineers inspecting earthquake damage have reported sill anchor bolts that actually split out of the concrete. To reduce the likelihood of this, place a continuous piece of concrete reinforcing steel to the outside of anchor bolts along slab edges. For stemwalls, place the anchor bolts between a pair of continuous bars at the top of the concrete or masonry. For sheet metal anchors, place a continuous bar inside the anchor's hook.

- For the cost of a large pizza you can increase the strength of your house's connection to the footing by about 25 percent. If they are not already required, use $5/_8$-inch anchor bolts in place of $1/_2$-inch bolts at all shear wall segments. You pay about 40 cents more per bolt, but the installation costs do not change.

- Use framing connectors instead of toenails to connect rim joists and blocks to the framing below. Toenails tend to split lumber (especially engineered lumber) and do not provide as strong a connection as face nails. The limitation on allowable load (150 plf) for toenailed connections often make framing connectors necessary. If your plans do not show this as an alternative to toe-nailing, you can do both. That way your inspector will be satisfied that you provided the toe-nails specified on the plans.

- Use spiked washers at anchor bolts before installing the mudsills. KC Metals' "MSP" is essentially a square washer with the corners bent straight up. You slip this over an anchor bolt before installing the sill, with the "teeth" pointing up so they embed in the mudsill when you tighten the nut on the anchor bolt. This provides a better grip on the sill, and increases the anchor bolt's holding power substantially. You can also place these on top of the mudsill under the standard nut and washer used to fasten the sill. (The company that originally manufactured these performed tests showing connection capacity was increased by about 90 percent for a toothed washer installed under the sill; installing a washer on top of the sill provided about a 60 percent increase, and using them both top and bottom increased capacity by about 140 percent. The testing approval reports are out of date, so the washers are not currently approved for increasing connection capacity. Even if they are not currently recognized by the code, toothed washers will substantially increase the strength of your mudsill connections; for around 50 cents each, these are a great bargain.)

INTERNAL STRENGTH—MAKING THE WALL STRONG

ENOUGH TO RESIST THE LOAD

3.4.1 Provide adequate panel nailing

You must nail the panels along all edges with the nail size and spacing shown on the plans. This seems obvious. Unfortunately, plans do not always provide adequate information regarding shear walls. Sometimes plans ambiguously call for "shear nailing." Does this mean 6-penny nails at 6 inches, or 10-penny nails at 2 inches? Considering how important shear walls are to keeping your house standing, it pays to have your plans prepared by an engineer who really does know what to specify.

Keep track of the panel nailing as your work progresses. Many builders tack several shear panels in place and come back later to install all the remaining nails. Inspectors occasionally find edges of panels without any nails in them. Panel nailing is boring—but you need to find a way that works for you to tell whether you have completed it. Some carpenters spray-paint the heads on strips of gun nails with a bright color to make it easier to tell which panels have been nailed. Choose a color that contrasts with the panels—bright blue or green may be a better choice against OSB than fluorescent orange. Marking the panels with kiel or spray-paint after nailing them would also work.

Some designs may require different nail spacing for shear wall segments along the same wall of a building, or even for areas of the same wall. New code provisions recognize that the stiffness of various shear wall segments depends on how narrow they are. Narrow walls will deflect (rack) more than wide walls of the same height and nailing schedule; to make the deflections match, a closer nailing pattern may be needed for narrower wall segments. It is even possible that wall areas next to window openings will need more nails than the areas below the windows. Designers should clearly show all unusual nailing requirements like these, preferably with an elevation view of the shear wall.

3.4.2 Use common nails if required

The table where most engineers get their design values for shear walls requires common or galvanized box nails. The APA did its original testing in the 1950s using these two types of nails. In the intervening half a century, common and box nails have mostly given way to sinkers or gun nails that can really only be identified by length and diameter.

You must consider nail length, head size and shank diameter when selecting the best fasteners. Shear panels resist loads by bearing against the nail shank to transfer a small amount of force into the stud or sill, and a larger shank provides more bearing area. Shear walls also fail (mostly during earthquakes) because of nail fatigue, where the nails actually break off just below the surface of the stud. The strength of the nails depends on their diameter and how strong the steel is. Common nails are thicker, but the wire used to make box nails is stronger.

Nail guns typically do not use nail sizes that correspond to the nails used in the APA shear wall tests. Although some nail manufacturers do make common nail sizes for nail guns, these may not be readily available and—according to representatives of two nail gun manufacturers—the most popular nail guns may not shoot them. The nail carton in Figure 35 shows how misleading nail labeling has become for gun nails. The label says "16-penny short"; the length noted corresponds to a 12-penny common nail, but the diameter is only that of an 8-penny common nail. The nails noted in Figure 36 as 8-penny coolers are shorter than an 8-penny common and have the diameter of a 6-penny common. Figure 37 shows a box of 10-penny plywood nails. The diameter of these nails does meet the code requirement for a 10-penny common nail. A 10-penny nail must have $1\frac{1}{2}$-inch penetration into the stud to develop its full capacity. If your shear wall was designed using the highest load in the APA tables, these $2\frac{1}{8}$-inch nails will work for shear panels up to $\frac{5}{8}$-inch thick.

More about nails...

The following table lists various nail sizes as given in ASTM (ASTM International) Specification F1667 (*Standard Specification for Driven Fasteners: Nails, Spikes, and Staples*). The building codes all refer to this specification. The table below also gives sample load capacities and minimum nail lengths when using Douglas Fir framing lumber.

Nail type	Length (inches)	Shank diameter (inches)	Head diameter (inches)	Allowable load in $1/2$-inch shear panel* (pounds)	Minimum penetration depth into framing required to achieve full load (inches)	Minimum length nail to achieve full load in $1/2$-inch shear panels
6d Cooler	$1^7/_8$	0.092		70**	$1^1/_8$	$1^5/_8$
6d Box	2	0.099	0.266	77**	$1^1/_4$	$1^3/_4$
6d Casing	$2^1/_4$	0.099		77	$1^1/_4$	$1^3/_4$
6d Siding	$1^7/_8$	0.106		Not Listed	$1^3/_8$	$1^7/_8$
6d Common	2	0.113	0.266	97	$1^3/_8$	$1^7/_8$
6d Ring- or Screw-Shank	2	0.120		Not Listed	$1^1/_2$	2
8d Cooler	$2^3/_8$	0.113		97	$1^3/_8$	$1^7/_8$
8d Box	$2^1/_2$	0.113	0.297	97	$1^3/_8$	$1^7/_8$
8d Casing	$2^1/_2$	0.113		97	$1^3/_8$	$1^7/_8$
8d Siding	$2^3/_8$	0.128		Not Listed	$1^5/_8$	$2^1/_8$
8d Sinker	$2^3/_8$	0.113	0.266	97	$1^3/_8$	$1^7/_8$
8d Common	$2^1/_2$	0.131	0.281	127	$1^5/_8$	$2^1/_8$
8d Ring- or Screw-Shank	$2^1/_2$	0.120		110	$1^1/_2$	2
10d Box	3	0.128	0.312	***	$1^5/_8$	$2^1/_8$
10d Common	3	0.148	0.312	155	$1^7/_8$	$1^3/_8$
10d Ring- or Screw-Shank				Not Listed		
12d Common	$3^1/_4$	0.148	0.312	N/A	$1^7/_8$	$1^3/_8$
16d Box	$3^1/_2$	0.135	0.344	N/A	$1^5/_8$	$2^1/_8$
16d Sinker	$3^1/_4$	0.148	0.344	N/A	$1^7/_8$	
16d Common	$3^1/_2$	0.162	0.344	N/A	2	

Designers would be wise to check on what carpenters typically use in their area, and builders should verify that the nails they plan to use in shear wall construction conform to the engineering requirements. The information in ESR-1539 is not as widely known as it should be. Some designers do not know that nails besides common or galvanized box are code-approved. If you really need to substitute gun nails on a job where common or galvanized box nails were specified, ask the designer if he or she has a copy of ESR-1539[10] (and expect to pay for the designer's time spent to verify or revise your proposed substitution). Using anything besides the nails specified on the plans would be hard to explain in court, even if "everyone else uses these other nails." To help clarify the problem with nail sizes, a code change to the 2006 IBC by ISANTA added the actual size (length and diameter) of nails in all of the fastening tables in Chapter 23.

* For comparison purposes only—based on one-half of the allowable shear per foot in a shear wall with nail spacing at 6 inches, from ESR 1539[10]

** For load shown for these shank diameters, ESR 1539[10] requires minimum nail length of $2^1/_4$ inches. This indicates that only 6-penny *casing* nails meet the requirements for shear wall nailing.

*** Value not listed in ESR 1539[10], but IBC tables (based on the APA's tests) give equal values for common and galvanized box nails. The load value from IBC Table 2306.3 for 6-inch nail spacing is 340 pounds per foot, giving 170 pounds per nail.

The above three footnotes show how quickly things can become confusing. It would take several more footnotes to clarify everything in this table for all the conditions that might arise.

Carpenters and engineers almost universally complain that too many different nail sizes are available and that there is a lack of standardization for nails. While I agree that the choices of nails can cause confusion, this is not because of a lack of standards for the nails themselves. ASTM Specification F1667 lists many different types of nails: common, box, cooler, brad, casing, siding, shingle, roofing, sinker, masonry, drywall, etc. This has given us so many choices that it is almost paralyzing.

Limiting the variety of fasteners allowed for structural connections could make job-site life simpler. (Choosing which fasteners to list could keep code committees, nail and nail-gun manufacturers busy for quite awhile.) But limiting choices in nails is a double-edged sword. What happens when you run out of "shear wall nails"? Can you use those "siding" nails you have in the back of your truck at a closer spacing?

The best solution I see at this point is for designers to specify on the plans what types of nails are acceptable (by giving length, shank diameter and head size), and for the builder to use the specified nails or obtain the designer's approval for a substitution. Maybe in the future we will see nails with color-coded heads that indicate what strength level they provide in a shear wall, regardless of their dimensions. One manufacturer has already begun color coding nails to identify shank diameter and length. This could be tremendously helpful—unless another manufacturer starts using a different color-coding system. (Even this particular color-coding system lists one color as denoting either $2^1/_2$- or $3^1/_2$-inch nails with 0.162-inch diameter.)

3.4.3 Full round-head vs clipped-head nails

According to APA research, nail heads tend to pull through the shear panels at their ultimate load. Common and box nails have larger heads than most gun nails, especially "clipped" or "D-head" nails. Clipped-head nails blow through the outer plies of shear panels more easily than round-head nails; overdriven nails are discussed later. ESR 1539[10] does not restrict the use of clipped-head nails, but the local building official may require round-head nails—his or her authority can override ESR 1539 (IBC Section 104.1).

Figure 35
Labeled as 16-penny nails, these have neither the length nor diameter of a 16-penny common nail.

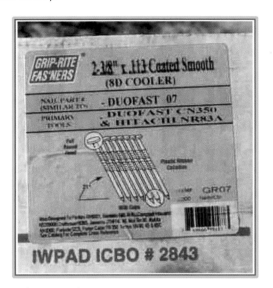

Figure 36
Eight-penny cooler nails have the diameter of a 6-penny common nail.

Figure 37
These nails really will substitute for 10-penny common nails when used for nailing shear panels up to $^5/_8$-inch thick.

Researchers at Virginia Polytechnic University tested clipped-head nails along with casing and box nails. All were 8-penny ($2^1/_2$ inches long, 0.113-inch shank diameter), driven through $^{15}/_{32}$-inch plywood into a 2 x 4 member. They tested one group of clipped-head nails with the clipped edges of their heads installed parallel to the load, and another group with the clipped edges perpendicular. In their tests the clipped-head nails performed just as well as the round-head nails. Their tests applied loads with very small movement of the joint at first, increasing the amount of movement gradually. I feel better about full round-head nails if for no other reason than they are not as easy to overdrive as clipped head nails.

Stanley-Bostich recently introduced their "Hurriquake" line of gun nails. These nails have oversized heads that resist pulling through sheathing, and ringed shanks that increase anchorage to the framing. They are made with shank diameters of 0.113 and 0.131 inches (the diameter of 6-penny and 8-penny common nails, respectively), both $2^{1}/_{2}$ inches long (the length of an 8-penny common). Researchers at Brigham Young University tested them in shear walls. Their research results suggest that the larger head can make up for using a smaller shank diameter. The oversized heads and ringed shanks also increase resistance to wind suction on walls or roofs.

So we have somewhat conflicting research results from two universities. While I wait for the next round of tests, I will recommend full round-head nails (or even oversized heads) with full "common" shank diameters. The increased cost of the nails is insignificant overall.

3.4.4 Do not use staples to connect shear panels in earthquake-prone areas

The model codes list allowable shear capacities for stapled shear walls. Recent tests have shown that stapled shear walls can fail because the thin staple legs fatigue and break underneath the shear panels at the face of the stud even though the staples look fine from the outside of the shear wall. Furthermore, this failure occurs with much less movement of the wall than shear walls fastened with nails can withstand. In early 2008, this potentially hidden failure led the Structural Engineers Association of California to request a code change that would forbid using staples to connect shear panels for seismic Design Categories C, D, E or F.

3.4.5 Install blocking behind horizontal panel joints

Remember that the perfect shear wall would be covered with a single enormous sheathing panel. If you need more than one panel, the panels must join over framing members or blocking. To give yourself a bigger target for nailing, install 2x flat blocking (this also leaves room for wiring and small plumbing lines). For heavier shear walls, you must use 3x or 4x blocking. A good shear wall schedule will tell you when you need 3x blocking. Fire-blocking may serve as backing for panel joints, but fire-blocking or blocking specifically shown or noted on the plans as full-depth cannot be laid flat.

Figure 38 shows a row of flat blocks installed behind panel joints. Figure 39 shows a row of 4 x 4 blocks. Note that the shear panels in the photo also extend all the way to the truss top chord.

You should not see daylight through a shear wall. The wall in Figure 40 should have blocks installed behind the joint below the windowsill. Although wall space below windows often does not serve as a shear wall, this particular wall section was intended to serve as one. The blocks beneath the window sill hint at this. (See the section entitled "Openings through Shear Walls" on Page 131.)

[Note: Blocking behind panel joints is not universally required by the codes. The SDPWS-08 requires blocking at wood structural panel joints, but allows unblocked joints if the designer considers the increased deflection and reduced strength of the wall and the edge-nailing is spaced no *closer* than 6 inches. (See SDPWS Section 4.3.7.1, Item 1.) For shear walls with unblocked panel joints the design strength of the wall must be reduced by as much as 60 percent compared to a blocked shear wall (SDPWS-08 Section 4.3.3, Table 4.3.3.2). Furthermore, unblocked shear walls will deflect more than blocked shear walls. Blocking is required in braced wall panels for Seismic Design Category D and E (Section 2308.12.4). The general requirement for braced wall panels in the lower seismic design categories (A, B and C) states, "Horizontal joints shall occur over blocking or other framing equal in size to the studding except where waived by the installation requirements for the specific sheathing materials." (Section 2308.9.3).]

Figure 38
Blocking behind horizontal panel joints allows for connection between panels

Figure 39
For heavier shear walls, use 3x or 4x blocks. Note that panels extend to roof diaphragm.

Figure 40
BAD—You should not see light through shear walls. Nothing transfers forces across this panel joint.

The APA asserts that an unblocked plywood or OSB braced wall will outperform any of the other bracing methods permitted under conventional light-frame construction such as let-in braces or gypsum wallboard. Panels nailed to studs without blocking at the horizontal joints will have at best 40 percent of the strength that blocked panels have. If you have a set of plans prepared by an engineer or architect, you do not have conventional light-frame construction and you must install blocking behind panel joints. At least one National Evaluation Report for OSB sheathing also requires blocking at horizontal joints when using panels in place of let-in bracing. This would include braced wall panels used in conventional construction. If you want to skip the horizontal blocking, make sure that the Evaluation Report does not require it for your sheathing. . . or find a really good attorney.

What can you do if the shear panels were installed without blocking behind the panel joints? Obviously, if you have access to the other side of the wall, you can install the blocks from behind and then nail along the panel joints into the blocks. But maybe someone already installed shear panels and you have no way to get behind them. Remember that you need to transfer horizontal forces from one panel to another across the horizontal panel joints. With horizontal blocking, a row of nails along each panel edge provides a way to transfer this force. You would have nailed along panel edges into the blocking at 6-inch spacing or less. Now you need to install a substitute for the blocking. Several options are presented next. If you are working on an engineered design, you must consult with the engineer before using any of the following methods.

1. If the blocking was overlooked, you will still have a few nails along the horizontal edges—one nail at each stud. For studs at 16 inches on center, you have "edge nails" every 16 inches. You can approximately double the force transfer by adding a second nail into each stud, above and below the panel joint. This would give you about the same strength as edge nailing at 8 inches. You do not want to split the studs though, so predrill for 8-penny or larger nails. You would not usually drive four nails into the edge of a stud

within 3 inches of each other! Unfortunately the greatest strength you could hope for from double-nailing is still less than the weakest properly-built shear wall.

2. If you have an engineered shear wall with very close edge nailing, you can still transfer shear forces across a panel joint without blocking behind it. Using wafer-head screws, attach a sheet metal framing connector such as Simpson's "LTP4" across the joint.

3. The APA's Technical Note No. N370C reports on strips of sheet-metal "blocking" installed over panel joints with pneumatically driven staples. The report gives the allowable load for each staple, based on the shear panel thickness, sheet metal gage and staple gage.

3.4.6 Avoid horizontal panel joints and blocking by using longer sheathing panels

Figure 41 shows a 9-foot-tall shear wall that the builder sheathed with 9-foot-long OSB panels (OSB is available in lengths up to 12 feet by special order in many areas). Note that panel thickness, stud spacing and other design considerations may dictate installing the panels oriented horizontally, in which case you cannot avoid installing blocking. Also, this will not help if your wall is over 10 feet tall, as fireblocking is required every 10 feet to prevent fire from spreading in wall cavities.

Figure 41
Nine-foot-tall panels eliminate the need for a row of horizontal blocks in this shear wall.

3.4.7 Use the specified lumber species

The tables that give allowable shear wall loads in the IBC specify shear panels attached to Douglas Fir-Larch or Southern Pine framing. These species groups give nails better holding capacity than other softwood species. Designers should specify the required wood species on the plans. Unless another species is specified, the safest course is to use Douglas Fir-Larch or Southern Pine framing. The required species must be used for all framing in shear walls, including footing sills and blocking behind panel joints.

Use caution when purchasing materials from "big-box" home improvement centers. Materials at such outlets may have been procured by someone 2,500 miles away who is unfamilar with local needs. I see "spruce-pine-fir" lumber frequently at warehouse stores.

For less dense species of framing lumber, the codes require designers to adjust the tabulated loads as follows:

For stapled shear walls (see Section 3.4.4 for warning regarding stapled shear walls in earthquake prone areas) using species groups with specific gravity between 0.42 or greater, use 82 percent of the values tabulated in the building code. These groups include the following:

Douglas Fir "south" (grown in the states of Arizona, New Mexico, Nevada and Utah) Eastern Hemlock Eastern Hemlock-Tamarack Eastern softwoods Eastern Spruce Hem-Fir	Mountain Hemlock Northern Pine Ponderosa Pine Red Pine Sitka Spruce Spruce-Pine-Fir (SPF) Western Hemlock Yellow Poplar

For stapled shear walls using species groups with specific gravity of 0.41 or less, use 65 percent of the tabulated values. These groups include the following:

Aspen Balsam Fir Coast Sitka Spruce Eastern White Pine	Engelmann Spruce-Alpine Fir Northern Species Northern White Cedar Western Cedars

For nailed shear walls with framing of other species, the code requires a reduction in the allowable shear values by the factor $[1-(0.5-SG)]$, where SG is the specific gravity of the species provided in the NDS. The reduction factor must be less than one. See footnote "a" of Table 2306.3.

For more information, see ESR 1539, Footnote 2 and Table A. Note that some of the above are "species groups" that may include several species. For instance, you won't find a "Hem-Fir" tree in the forest, but the Hem-Fir species group includes Western Hemlock and fir species including California Red, Grand, Noble, Pacific Silver and White. For more detailed information, re-fer to the NDS.

3.4.8 Use 3x framing members when needed

The code requires minimum 3x framing under panel joints in shear walls designed for a shear stress of more than 350 pounds per foot, or where panel edge nailing is 2 inches or less, or where 10-penny nails penetrate more than $1-1/2$ inches into framing and are spaced at 3 inches or less (SDPWS Section 4.3.7.1, Item 4). You can use 4x members if you cannot get 3x stock. Figure 39 shows 4x studs at panel joints. Some framers want to nail two 2x's together instead of using 3x or 4x members. The code specifically allows two 2-inch nominal members fastened together to transfer the design shear value between framing members (See footnote "i" of Table 2306.3, or the exception in SDPWS Section 4.3.7.1, Item 4). Although two thinner members together can work in theory, the number of nails needed could split studs if not carefully placed, and would al-most certainly split blocking between studs. I strongly advise against doubling up 2x stock. Chances are too great that the required additional nailing between the 2x's would not be installed or that the members would split. To avoid the 3x requirement an engineer would need to design the connection between the doubled members; as a ball-park figure you would need to stitch the members together with 16-penny common nails at the same spacing as the shear panel edge nailing.

3.4.9 Do not overdrive nails

A shear wall's strength depends largely on the thickness of sheathing that bears against the shank of each nail (see Figure 12). Note that the same applies to staples, if you use them to fas-ten the shear panels. Designers assume that the full thickness of the panels will bear against the nails. Nail heads must be driven flush with the surface of the sheathing (SDPWS Section 4.3.6.3). Oriented strand board can swell when it gets wet, which can result in the same appear-ance as overdriven nails. This is one reason that some engineers only permit plywood shear pan-els on exterior walls.

If you shoot nails through the top layer of sheathing, you should take some sort of corrective ac-tion. At best, you would need to add nails to give an adequate nail-bearing area. If more than 20 percent of fasteners are overdriven by more than $1/8$ inch, the APA suggests adding one new fas-tener for every two that are overdriven.[11] This solution works as long as the additional fasteners will not split the studs. The APA suggests using staples in cases where driving additional nails would tend to split framing members behind the shear panels. At worst, you might have to remove the panels and replace the studs behind them if they had split, and start over. Figures 42 through 45 show some severely overdriven nails. As an engineer said in an on-line forum, "lawyers in California get easy points for this one."

The APA acknowledges that two conditions do not require additional fasteners. First, if the shear panels installed are thicker than the panels specified, fasteners can be overdriven by the amount of additional thickness provided. Second, if the shear panels have swelled up around the fastener heads after they were installed (making it appear that the fasteners are overdriven, when they were actually installed correctly) then no additional fasteners are required.

You can avoid overdriven nails by hand-nailing (a good way to break in a new helper), using a nail gun with adjustable drive depth or turning the pressure down on your compressor or air regulator. If your nail gun leaves the nails standing slightly proud of the surface, you can use a hammer to flush-drive them fairly quickly.

Figure 42
Slightly overdriven nail

Figure 43
Badly overdriven nail.

Figure 44
Severely overdriven nail.

Figure 45
Nail? *What* nail?

All of the above photos show nailing variations, from bad to worse, on the same project. As one reviewer says, "Every framing contractor should have a nail gun with an adjustable nose piece." Apparently this framer did not.

3.4.10 Use studs free of wane

Wane is the loss of square corners on boards where tree bark was included in them during milling. Wane occurs in boards cut from the outer part of logs. Studs with wane will not provide full support behind shear panel edges, and you cannot nail the panels securely to them. Use pieces with wane where you can double them up or in places where shear panels will never meet; for example, king and trimmer studs, corner studs and top or bottom plates.

3.4.11 Provide adequate distance from nails to panel and stud edges

SDPWS Section 4.3.7.1, Item 2 requires a space of at least $3/_8$ inch from the centerline of the nail to the shear panel edge. Nails must be firmly driven into the framing members. In addition, the APA recommends installing panels with a $1/_8$-inch gap between them. It's easy to draw on plans, but for 2x studs these criteria demand very careful alignment of the panel joints and precisely placed nails to avoid splitting out the sides of the studs. This is one reason the code requires minimum 3x studs under panel joints in heavier shear walls. If you use 3x or 4x studs, remember to take advantage of them! Too often the person nailing off the shear panels will put in a row of nails $3/_8$ inch (or less) away from the panel edges, forgetting that the wider stud behind the panel would allow a lot more leeway for nail placement.

Figure 46 shows nailing that will tend to split out of the panel edges. If the worker nailing these panels had looked on the other side of the wall, he would have seen that panel joints occurred over 4 x 6 studs and that he had plenty of space to nail farther from the panel edges. Figure 47 shows panels installed by a structural engineer. Staggering the nails reduces the tendency to split framing members.

3.4.12 Stagger panel edge nailing

To reduce the chance of splitting framing members behind shear panels, the code requires that shear panel edge nailing is staggered if any of the following conditions apply: Nail spacing of 2 inches or less for any size nails; 10-penny common nails spaced at 3 inches or less; required capacity of shear wall exceeds 700 pounds per foot in Seismic Design Category D, E or F (SDPWS Section 4.3.7.1, Item 4). Staggering edge nailing is good practice in all other cases as well.

3.4.13 Check behind the wall for "shiners" after nailing off the sheathing

Once you finish nailing the shear panels, check to see that all the nails really hit the studs. Nails that just glance off the edge of the stud or miss it completely are known as shiners, and they do not give your wall any strength. Someone intent on suing a builder can buy a special periscope-like instrument that will poke into a small hole in a wall and reveal shiners. Mark any places where nailing missed the studs and install proper nailing. Removing any shiners will reduce the likelihood of them arousing concern later on.

3.4.14 Cut neat holes for electric boxes and the like

Figure 48 shows an all-too-common condition found around electric outlet boxes. This area of shear wall would be stronger if the electrician had cut out a round area shown in the circle. Even though the homeowner will never see it, a big enough earthquake will find this weak point. My favorite framers and electricians use 6-inch hole-saws to make holes for outlet boxes. On the other hand, I have also seen work by fire sprinkler installers who apparently used hand grenades to make holes through shear panels for their pipes. Figure 49 shows a neatly cut hole around an electric box.

3.4.15 Do not cut slots in shear walls

Several years ago I visited a site that had two shear walls designed to the maximum possible strength. These 4-foot-wide walls sat on either side of a glass storefront. The design needed every last inch of width in those walls. The contractor had installed a $14^1/_2$-inch-wide foundation vent at the base of each wall. "But it's just a *little* hole," said the contractor. A shear wall does not function as a sail—remember how the shear elements work. Almost one-third of the sheathing along the bottom plate was cut out to make this "little" hole. Imagine cutting just a "little" section out of your car's driveshaft.

The same problem occurs when other trades cut slots in shear panels. Figure 50 shows what happened when the plumber beat the carpenters to the site, and a shear panel had to slide down over the water supply line. Figure 51 shows a shear wall that has had much of its capacity sacrificed to gas service lines for separate condominium units. This should have been addressed during design, or, had the designer been hired to make periodic site visits, could have been remedied during construction.

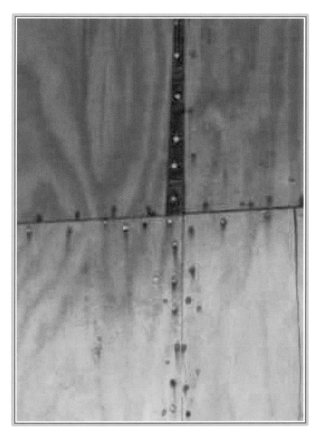

Figure 46
BAD—Too many nails too close to the panel edges could tear out of these panels.

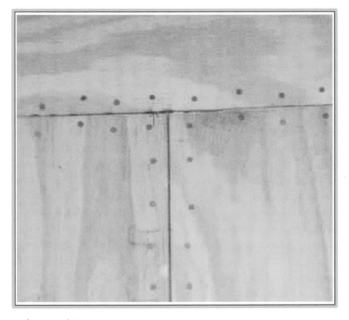

Figure 47
GOOD—Nails installed with adequate edge distance will not tear out of panel edges. Slight stagger will help prevent studs and plates from splitting. Nailing shown is into framing wider than a single 2x stud.

Figure 48

BAD—Overcuts weaken shear panels by providing starting places for the panel to tear.

Figure 49

GOOD—This neatly cut hole will not significantly reduce the shear wall's strength.

The slot in Figure 50 could be repaired by securing a strip of shear panel on the back side of the sheathing. A small notch at the top of the strip could fit around the waterline. The sheathing strip would need to overlap the sides of the slot by a couple of inches and would have to connect to the main shear panel to match the capacity of the shear panel edge nailing. If there was not room to slip a sheathing "patch" into the space behind the wall sheathing, then one could use a variation of the sheet-metal blocking described on Page 56. The designer would need to specify either type of repair. The slots shown in Figure 51 do not give the opportunity for such a remedy; addressing this situation will take a fair amount of consideration by the designer. (Hint: this looks a lot like Figure 132, if you had a very low window with pipes running through it.)

Figure 50
BAD—Vertical slot at water line is a built-in weakness.

Figure 51
BAD—Horizontal slots at gas lines form a line of weakness in this shear wall.

3.4.16 Nail T1-11 and other grooved siding through the full panel thickness and on both sides of joints—not just through the overlapping piece

The APA refers to grooved siding as Type 303 siding. (Commonly referred to as "T1-11," Type 303 siding includes many grooved patterns; T1-11 is just one of them.) Grooved plywood siding can also serve the purpose of shear paneling when properly installed.

Note that creating the grooves in Type 303 siding defeats one of the advantages of using plywood in the first place. Plywood's great strength comes mostly from the different layers of veneer with which it is made. Defects in veneer layers rarely align in such a way that any particular area of the panel has appreciable loss of strength. However, if you cut half-way through the plywood thickness to form grooves you take away some of that safety margin. Some observers reported that the Northridge earthquake caused serious failures of Type 303 siding along the grooves in the panels.

Two principles discussed earlier warrant repeating as they apply to grooved siding. First, the thickness of the siding that will serve as a shear wall is the thickness that you drive the nails through (see Footnote g in IBC Table 2306.3). The grooves typically are about one-half the plywood thickness. You must nail through the full thickness of the panels in order to transfer the full shear forces from one panel to the adjacent one.

The other concern is nailing along all the panel edges. To hasten installation, grooved siding is often installed by nailing only through the panel that overlaps the joint. The APA does *not* recommend this. A detail in their *Residential and Commercial Design Guide*[12] specifically notes *"Nailing of both panel edges along shiplap joint is recommended.* **The 'double nailing' is required when wall segment must meet wall bracing or engineered shear wall requirements.***"* For wider groove patterns such as reverse board-and-batten, and for easier nailing of shiplap siding, use 3x minimum studs behind panel joints. Figure 52 shows a panel joint in a shear wall that can only rely on friction between the panels. Figure 53 shows a house that failed in the 2003 San Simeon Earthquake. This was the only recently-built house to suffer major damage in that quake, and faulty nailing of the grooved plywood siding was the main cause of failure.

3.4.17 Pay special attention to walls with shear panels installed on both sides

Sometimes a relatively short length of wall must resist very large lateral forces. In this case, the engineer may call for shear panels on both sides of the wall segment.

To avoid splitting the studs when driving two rows of nails into their opposite edges at panel joints, either stagger the panel joints along the two sides of the wall or use 3x minimum studs (if 3x's are not already required for the nailing pattern). A footnote in the code shear wall tables requires this (IBC Table 2306.3, footnote h).

If the plans show shear panels on both sides of the wall, do not put two layers of shear paneling on one side of the wall. Several years ago I designed a repair job for a restroom plumbing wall that was supposed to have plywood on both sides of it. Both layers of plywood had been placed on the side of the wall away from the plumbing. Panels in the top layer were nailed through the first layer. At panel joints in the second layer, the shear from both layers of plywood was taken by only the first layer. Other problems with such an installation include splitting framing members where they receive twice as many nails into one face of the member, and unequal performance of the two layers of sheathing. Although wise designers and carpenters place shear panels on the "safest" side of plumbing walls and such, the safe side of this wall was already used by the first layer of plywood.

3.4.26 Use minimum 4x8 sheathing panels

Section 4.3.7.1, Item 1 of the SDPWS requires a minimum shear panel size of 4 by 8 foot except at boundaries and changes in framing.

3.4.27 Using adhesives to attach shear panels is prohibited in higher seismic design categories

Section 4.3.6.3.1 of the SDPWS prohibits attaching shear panels with adhesives except for special cases in Seismic Design Categories A, B and C, and then only if certain design conditions are met. Adhesive attachment makes shear walls stiffer; earthquake forces increase for stiffer walls, so the designer will have to increase the design strength of the wall *and the rest of the earthquake force resisting system*. Using adhesives also makes the connections more brittle (less ductile). When nails attaching shear panels bend back and forth during an earthquake, a great deal of energy is absorbed; adhesive connections tend to fail suddenly without absorbing as much energy from the earthquake.

An alert editor at the *Journal of Light Construction* points out that spray-on foam insulation may act the same as adhesive. Conscientious builders often use a thin coat of closed cell spray-foam for air-sealing exterior walls, or even to fill the entire wall cavity. I am not aware of any research into the combined use of spray-foam with shear walls, and suggest using other air-sealing methods such as taping the seams of shear panels (note that caulking around panels could also act the same as adhesive.)

3.4.28 Nail consistently along all panel edges

Installing extra nails or rows of nails unevenly around a shear wall reduces overall performance. See Section 3.7.5 on Page 89.

3.4.29 Above and beyond the code

You can make many simple changes that will improve a shear wall's internal strength.

● Use nails with extra large heads; they will not tear through shear panels as easily as standard nails. Nails such as Stanley-Bostich's "Hurriquake" nails have oversized heads. These nails come in an 8-penny common size (0.131-inch-diameter shank, $2\frac{1}{2}$ inches long) advertised as having "up to 25 percent more effective head area." One assumes this means 25 percent more head area than a common nail.

● Use the next size larger nails (up to 10 penny). Nails are cheap. However, for 10-penny nail spacing of 3 inches or less, you will need 3x studs at panel joints.

● Use more nails. This will add to your labor, but 50 percent more nails around the shear panel edges essentially means a 50-percent stronger shear wall. The overall labor increase is much less than 50 percent; you have already cut and installed all the panels. (Nails spaced closer than 3 inches on center may require 3x studs at panel joints. See also note above regarding 10-penny nails, and Section 3.1.4 regarding special inspection; the Structural Engineers Association of California suggests that special inspection should not be required if the original design did not require nails at less than 4-inch spacing.)

- Use five-layer, five-ply plywood. The IBC does not differentiate between plywood and OSB; they are both considered "wood structural panels." However, engineers investigating failures after recent earthquakes observed that five-ply plywood seemed to hold up the best in shear walls. Preliminary APA tests indicated that walls sheathed with OSB failed at slightly lower loads during cyclic testing. (This was because of the nails, not the sheathing. The OSB is actually more dense than plywood, and causes nails to fatigue and break sooner. See Reference 9.) According to the APA, extensive testing has shown no significant difference in the way plywood and OSB perform. This is under laboratory conditions, though—OSB and plywood can behave differently in the field. When OSB gets wet it swells more than plywood. When it swells, it can either pull the nails out slightly or swell up around the nail heads. In the first case you have a loose nail; in the second case you have a nail that looks and performs as if it was overdriven. Exterior wall finishes should keep sheathing dry but do occasionally fail. Reports from contractors who repair OSB damaged by trapped moisture in walls suggest that OSB is not suitable for exterior walls, at least while current weatherproofing techniques (some of which are code mandated) are in use. For this reason some engineers require plywood on exterior walls.

- Use thicker panels. For a dollar or two per sheet, you can upgrade to the next thicker shear panel. This can increase the shear capacity of the wall up to 20 percent. Engineers familiar with damage caused by the 1994 Northridge earthquake recommend $1/_2$-inch minimum panel thickness.

- When nailing panels to pressure-treated sills at footings, install about 20 to 25 percent extra nails. This will address two issues: First, pressure-treated material is often softer than the lumber specified for shear wall framing (see "Construction problems can compound each other" on Page 29). Second, west coast wood species are typically incised so that they will accept treatment chemicals more easily. The extra nails will help make up for the outer layer of wood that is degraded by the incising process. (This recommendation typically will not apply in areas using Southern Pine lumber, as Southern Pine gives the intended fastening strength for the sill and accepts chemical treatment well without incising.)

- Use seasoned (dry) lumber. In one series of tests APA—The Engineered Wood Association built eight shear wall specimens; six were fabricated using unseasoned lumber (moisture content above 19 percent—such lumber is usually stamped "S-Grn" on the grade stamp). They waited several months for the specimens to dry out, and then tested the walls along with two specimens built with dry lumber. The walls had similar ultimate strengths, but walls built with seasoned lumber were about twice as stiff as the others (see APA Report No. T2002-53); remember that the best way to limit damage to your home's finishes is to reduce the deflection of the wall, accomplished by increasing the stiffness.

- Provide a positive moisture barrier between a concrete footing and the shear panels. Concrete is far from waterproof. It wicks a good deal of moisture out of the ground, and if your shear panels touch the slab or stemwall you may end up with a row of nails into a dry-rotted shear panel. In dry climates, installing the panel with a $1/_2$-inch gap to the concrete may eliminate this problem. A pressure-treated sill is not waterproof either—it may wick enough moisture into the shear panels to eventually weaken the panel, especially in moist climates. Solutions to this could include galvanized or "peel-and-stick" flashing between the sill and the sheathing.

● Install shear panels with $1/8$-inch gaps at all joints, if not already required by the manufacturer's installation instructions. As explained earlier, this will allow the panels to expand without buckling.

Tie-downs—Keeping your shear walls from rocking up and down during an earthquake or rolling over in a windstorm

Besides the obvious cases of omitting tie-downs altogether, many pitfalls await the framer. The worst usually involve the owner showing up and asking, "Could we make this window wider?" just after you have nailed off the shear panels and attached a tie-down to the king and trimmer studs.

3.5.1 Placement of tie-downs

Wide shear walls perform better than narrow ones. Shear paneling installed beyond end-posts (the posts with tie-downs) is theoretically useless, so if a shear wall needs tie-downs, they should be installed on posts placed as far apart as possible. Put another way, the tie-down posts define the ends of the shear wall. (The "Quick Start" figure inside the book cover shows a tie-down installed just away from the corner post. This was shown to illustrate that if the tie-down is not attached to the end-post of the wall, the panel edge nailing is required at the tie-down post. This illustration was NOT intended to suggest moving tie-downs away from the end of walls.)

Where exactly should you locate a tie-down on the shear wall end-post? At the bottom? Toward the inside of the shear wall, or on the outside? For a single tie-down attached to a post, studies show that shear walls perform better when the tie-down attaches to the inside of the post (the side of the post toward the center of the shear wall). As for the height of the tie-down, in theory you can install it at any convenient height—sometimes even on the floor above the shear wall! Remember that the tie-down only needs to exert a downward force on the shear wall end-post; it will work whether it pushes down on the top of the post or pulls on the bottom of it. Theory is one thing, code-approvals and testing are another—Simpson Strong-Tie has tested their tie-downs for placement up to 18 inches off the floor; unless the approved plans indicate otherwise you must follow the tie-down manufacturer's installation instructions.

3.5.2 Install all required connectors from the tie-down to the post and footing

For whatever reason, inspectors find many instances of inadequately installed tie-downs. When you have completed the framing, make a point of systematically checking every tie-down; otherwise you may as well leave them on the shelf at the lumberyard.

Many shear walls will lift right off their footings because no nut was ever installed on the anchor rod from the footing. Figure 58 shows a tie-down that will not begin to work until the shear wall end-post lifts a few inches off the slab. The tie-down in Figure 59 connects to the footing;

but will the framers make the struggle to nail it to the post? In this case a "palm-nailer" might fit between the studs, but that is about the only way to connect this tie-down besides removing the studs to the left that obstruct nailing. The connection in Figure 60 looks good until you realize that the hex-head bolt has only one or two threads extending into the coupling nut. A $\frac{5}{8}$-inch-diameter bolt needs at least $\frac{5}{8}$ inch of thread engagement to develop full connection strength.

Figure 58

Loose nut on anchor rod will allow this end-post to lift off the slab, resulting in severe damage. Note: Current manufacturer's literature requires reversing the bolts to the end post. See Section 3.5.22.

Figure 59

Nailing this tie-down to the post will require using a palm-nailer or removing the double studs.

3.5.3 Do not bend tie-down straps embedded in the footings down and back up more than one time

Manufacturers' catalogs indicate that straps for embedded tie-downs will fatigue if bent more than one cycle down (to get them out of the way during construction) and then back up to attach to the shear wall end-post. If you bend a strap and it has visible cracks in it, or if the concrete has spalled where the anchor is embedded, the connection strength is reduced. At least one hardware manufacturer has technical bulletins that discuss this strength reduction. The spalling in Figure 62 would be considered excessive.

3.5.4 Nail the sheathing securely to the post that has the tie-down attached to it

The monotony of nailing off six acres of shear panels can lull workers into a routine of nailing panel edges at the required edge nailing and field nailing everywhere else. Many times, posts with tie-downs do not fall at panel edges or even on the regular framing layout. Prominently mark tie-down post locations so that they will receive proper nailing. The photo in Figure 62 shows inadequate sheathing nailing to the tie-down post. The nailing to the post should match the edge nailing at the panel joint to the right of the tie-down. It is even easier to overlook this additional nailing when the tie-down bracket connected to the post is hidden behind the panels. At least this strap reminds the carpenter that there is a post behind the sheathing. On the other hand, Figure 63 shows a row of closely spaced nails nowhere near the panel edge. Figure 64 shows the other side of this wall; the installer remembered that the force in the plywood needed to get to the post connected to the footing.

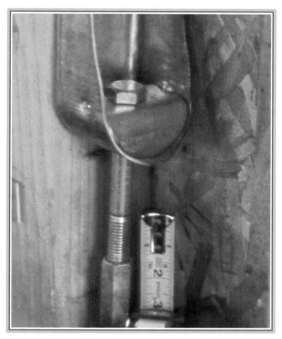

Figure 60
Standard thread length on a $^5/_8$- inch bolt is $1^1/_2$ inches, leaving almost no thread engagement with the coupler.

3.5.5 Install tie-downs to full-height posts

Tie-downs need to transfer uplift forces from the full height of the shear wall to the footing. Figure 61 shows a tie-down attached to the end of a pony wall. Unless shear panels are installed on the pony wall, the full-height portion will never even know there is a tie-down nearby. Even then, without significant reinforcement the partial-height portion of this wall will stay put as the full-height portion rips up and away in an earthquake or windstorm.

3.5.6 Tie shear walls across floor levels

Most literature on shear walls shows single-story walls constructed on slab footings. Tie-down forces from shear walls above the ground floor must end up in the footing. Figure 65 shows a strap from a second-floor shear wall that connects it to the first-floor framing, with one problem. The strap bends in at the rim joist, which creates a slight amount of slack in it. Similarly when a wet sawn lumber rim joist dries and shrinks, a strap installed across it will form an outward bulge. Before such straps will carry any load, they must straighten out. Figure 66 shows a strap installed correctly so that it will not let the upper-level shear wall lift up appreciably; the engineered wood rim joist will not shrink. The lower floor post that the strap connects to must have a tie-down attached to it that secures it to the footing in almost all cases. The all-thread rods shown in Figure 67 extend to tie-downs on each side of a post in a shear wall above.

Figure 61
Strap tie-down at right of partial-height wall will not anchor the whole wall.

Some connector manufacturers' catalogs list "clear span" lengths for straps when used to tie across floor levels or in similar applications. The minimum strap length required is the clear span length plus the length needed to adequately connect the strap to the posts above and below the floor platform. In Figures 65 and 66, the clear span distance is the width of the rim joist plus the thickness of the top and bottom plates. Nails within the clear span do not contribute to the connection from the first-floor post to the second-floor post. Strap manufacturers tell you how many nails to install in each end of the strap. For the connections shown, these nails must all go into the posts.

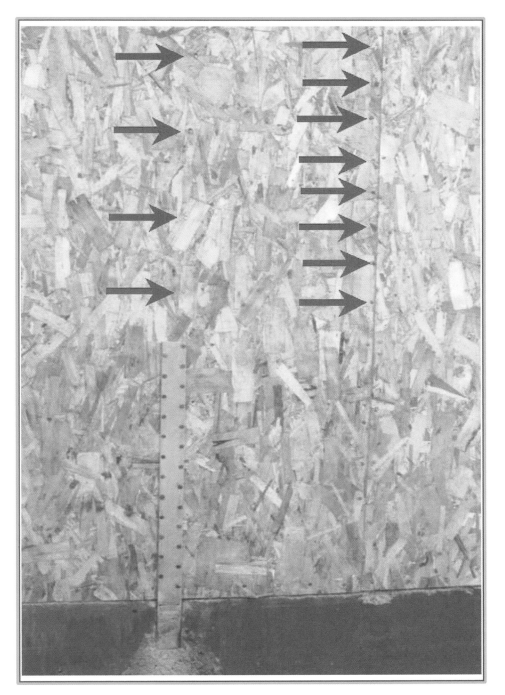

Figure 62

This strap tie-down was bent after the concrete was poured, which spalled the concrete and did not enhance the strength of the strap. The arrows highlight panel nailing. Nailing to the post behind the strap tie-down should match the panel edge nailing, but only about half the required nails are present.

Figure 63

Vertical row of nails in center of panel at "edge-nail" spacing. This photo also shows holes cut neatly around outlet boxes. Figure 64 shows what the center row of nails connects to.

Figure 64

View from other side of wall shown in Figure 63 shows post with tie-down. This tie-down was installed to allow the electrician to bore holes at a convenient height for running wire.

Figure 65
BAD—Bend in strap tie-down will cause it to perform poorly.

Figure 66
GOOD—Correctly installed strap with no slack.

Figure 67
These threaded rods extend to a shear wall
end-post at the floor above. The joist blocking will also provide bearing capacity for the
post above.

Houses with raised floors need similar connections. If the first-floor framing rests on cripple
walls, you must extend anchor rods to tie-downs at the main level walls. If you anchor only to
the post in the cripple wall, only the cripple wall will remain intact after a storm or earthquake.

Figure 68 shows a threaded rod stubbed above a cripple wall. A coupling nut with another
length of rod will extend to a tie-down above, once the floor and walls are framed. Notice the
4 x 4 cripple post—this will provide bearing capacity under the shear wall end-post above.

Strap-type tie-downs are available with additional length to extend up over a rim joist and then
nail onto the shear wall end stud, but they will not bridge the height of a cripple wall. Treat a
cripple wall as the case illustrated in Figure 66, by anchoring the cripple post and then strapping from it up to the main-wall framing above.

3.5.7 Tie shear frames in attics in line with shear wall end-posts

Blending Sections 3.5.4 and 3.5.6 brings us to this requirement. Nine- or ten-foot-tall shear
walls are common in today's custom homes. These shear walls may extend that much or more
above the ceiling in the form of shear frames between roof trusses, as shown in Figure 69. The
portion of the shear wall above the ceiling must also have tie-downs at both ends.

Figure 68
This threaded rod will extend to a shear wall end-post at the main floor, and the 4 × 4 cripple post will provide bearing capacity for the end-post.

Figure 69
Tall shear frames like these may require large tie-down forces at each end of the shear wall.

The plans should detail this connection. A strap from the lower end-post across the ceiling framing to a post in the shear frames might serve the purpose. Designers will sometimes call for attaching the tie-down to the framing above the ceiling and extending the anchor rod from the footing up into the attic. In any case, tie-down design and installation must account for the additional height of shear wall above the ceiling level.

3.5.8 Provide a continuous load path to the footing for the tie-down force

Sometimes the tie-down force cannot get directly from the shear wall end-post to the footing. The end of the second-floor shear wall segment in the upper right corner of Figure 70 aligns over a doorway. Note the strap going from the end-post down across the second-floor platform and connecting to a cripple post over the door header. This system is one strap short of being complete, as Figure 71 shows from the inside. Straps tie both ends of the header to its support posts, but nothing connects the cripple post to the middle of the header.

Figure 70
Outside view—Strap over doorway looks good from the outside, but Figure 71 reveals a gap in the load path.

Designing a continuous load path can take considerable effort. Some hardware manufacturers' literature shows oversimplified "artist's concepts" of a complete load path. These drawings can mislead people as to the true nature of the load path.

3.5.13 Install new anchors if needed because of plan changes or major layout errors

One of my favorite clients calls me once in a while to report he has made a field change, "but don't worry, its nothing structural." One such call required several hours of engineering and then just as much time for a carpentry crew to address. Our client had put a closet opening where I had designed the end-post under three stories' worth of shear walls. The designer must affirm changes to approved plans. Even changes that may look nonstructural can have a huge effect on a building's lateral strength.

Figures 78 through 80 show cases where the end of the shear wall was relocated during construction. In cases with strap tie-downs, abandon the strap and install a bracket-type tie-down to the relocated end-post of the shear wall segment. To anchor this new tie-down to the footing, you must drill a hole in the footing in the proper location and set a new anchor rod in it with a suitable adhesive or pourable anchoring cement. The designer must specify anchor size, location, embedment depth, adhesive type and so forth.

Figure 78
California requires seismic straps at water heaters, but this is not what they had in mind. (A new tie-down was installed on the other side of the shear wall to the right of the water heater platform.)

Figure 79
Owner wanted a wider window, leaving this tie-down strap flapping in the wind.

In some cases, leaning the tie-down anchor rod, as described in the previous section, just will not work. Figure 80 shows a 4 x 12 used to shim between a tie-down bracket and the relocated shear wall end-post. In the first edition of this book I suggested that this configuration could work if the 4 x 12 was connected at top and bottom to prevent it from rotating. This suggestion did not fully consider the geometry of the connection. In the installation shown, the connection will experience uplift forces when earthquake or wind forces act to the right. The bigger problem in this connection is the additional force due to leverage on the system. The king and trimmer studs will lean to the right under load; as they do so the 4 x 12 block will lean as well, acting as a lever that will pry the tie-down bracket up with great force as the block tends to rock up on its lower-right corner. The 4 x 12 block should be removed and a new tie-down installed to the window king and trimmer studs.

Figure 80
This 4 × 12 spacer between the tie-down and the window king and trimmer studs will not perform as hoped.

3.5.14 Lag bolts are generally not adequate as tie-down anchors

A few years ago I photographed a tie-down that was simply lagged through the first floor sill, floor sheathing and the top plate of the cripple wall below, similar to the connection shown in Figure 81. The photo won third place in Simpson Strong-Tie's annual "Misinstallation" contest and appears briefly in the video "Understanding Earthquake Forces."[13] Advanced shear wall systems may use tie-downs lagged to beams below, but lagging to standard framing cannot provide the uplift resistance most shear walls need. Anchoring a shear wall will require a large lag bolt sunk into a hefty wood member, which in turn must have both ends connected to resist uplift. A licensed designer will need to specify such a connection, which typically might have a maximum capacity of around 2,500 pounds—not very impressive as tie-downs go.

3.5.15 Attach tie-downs directly to the shear wall end-post

Figure 81 also shows a tie-down with a filler block between it and the shear wall end-post. This filler will allow the connection to flex more than a bracket attached directly to the stud and will tend to pry the connection apart. None of the connector manufacturers' catalogs show the sort of attachment pictured here. The following item discusses a similar problem when using multiple studs.

Figure 81

Lag screws can anchor tie-downs, but not like this. Tie-down brackets should also attach directly to the end-post.

3.5.16 Connect multiple studs securely when used as end-posts

Some manufacturers' catalogs give tie-down capacities for double studs. One catalog notes that the designer must determine how to connect the studs. Another adds that the fasteners specified in their catalog for the tie-down "shall not be considered to attach multiple plies together." Your plans should tell you how to connect multiple studs if they give the option for using them. Proper connection between studs will typically need 16-penny nails at 4- to 12-inch spacing—many more nails than a common built-up stud.

3.5.17 Install all nails in off-the-shelf straps or tie-downs

Figure 82 shows a tie-down that was not secured fully to the end-post (luckily for the plumber). This lack of complete nailing has reduced the tie-down's capacity by the fraction of the nails that are missing. Connector manufacturers' catalogs all state something like, "use all specified fasteners." One way to repair this would be to install wafer-head screws that are just short enough to miss the drain line, provided there is at least an inch or so left for screw embedment and tensile capacity of the post. You could also attach an extension strap using heavy sheet metal screws and then nail the extension to the end-post. Either of these solutions must come from the designer.

Figure 82
This strap tie-down lost about 20 percent of its capacity to avoid nailing into the sink drain. In addition, the large hole bored through the post for the pipe weakens it.

3.5.18 Do not drill large holes through end-posts

Figure 82 also shows a shear wall end-post with a $2\frac{1}{2}$-inch-diameter hole drilled through it. To resist uplift at this end of the shear wall, the tie-down strap secures the post to the footing. The end-post transfers this anchoring force to the vertical edge of the shear panel. The strap pulls down on the bottom of the post while the shear panels pull up on it. This tug-of-war can result in huge tension forces in the end-post (and also bending forces, depending on the geometry of the end-post and tie-down). If too much of the post was lost to plumbers or electricians it will snap apart and leave just a stub anchored to the footing. Several manufacturers make hardware to reinforce around holes in studs. Posts must also resist compression (which the following section discusses), and simply reinforcing at holes in posts to carry tension will not address this.

Often, the engineer who designs the shear walls in a house will not know where plumbing runs will go. Many jurisdictions require residential plans to show only the locations of plumbing fixtures, or at most a schematic piping layout. This means that the plumber may make up most of the piping design while installing it. If you find large holes bored through shear wall components, check with the designer to see what steps to take to reinforce them. These requirements vary with each shear wall and therefore are hard to put into a generic note on a shear wall schedule. A good rule of thumb would be to limit hole sizes to the average knot size you see in the post.

3.5.19 Pour larger footings if needed to resist uplift forces

Tie-downs listed in manufacturers' catalogs have capacities of up to 19,000 pounds (enough to lift two or three fully loaded pick-up trucks). Shear walls which need that much overturning resistance obviously should not just be anchored to a 2-foot-square, 12-inch-deep pad. When carpenters arrive on the scene, they should not have to worry about footing sizes. The designer should calculate the size footing required and show it on the foundation plan. If pads seem undersized, call the designer. Figure 83 shows a 2-foot, 6-inch-square pad at the left end of the strip footing. The photo does not show that this footing is 3 feet deep. The two anchor bolts at the left end of the placing template will connect to large tie-downs on both sides of a shear-wall end-post. (Some designers object to using multiple tie-downs on the same post, but if they are installed properly they will actually function better than just a single tie-down—see the second item under Section 3.5.24, "Above and beyond the code."

3.5.20 Anchor rods for tie-downs should run through loose holes in framing

We want holes to fit tightly around mudsill anchors so the mudsill does not slide. Conversely, holes drilled through framing to extend anchor rods for tie-downs should be loose. There are a few reasons for this; first, over-sized holes make it much easier to install the rods. Second, there is less chance that you will need to bend the rods to run through misaligned holes. Third, in the case where shrinkage-compensating devices are used (see Section 4.4) the anchor rod must not bind in holes between floors. Lastly, there is no reason that the tie-down anchor rod needs to bear against wood except as noted in the following section.

3.5.21 Get approval before using a tie-down anchor rod to serve double-duty as a mudsill anchor

In our theoretical shear wall, mudsill anchors resist sliding of the mudsill and tie-down anchors resist uplift. Can you combine both functions in the same anchor? Probably; but you will need to consult with the engineer. An anchor rod has a certain capacity to resist uplift; it also has a certain capacity to resist shear. If you load it fully in uplift and shear at the same time, though,

Figure 84
BAD—Strap will carry tension loads (after it gets nailed to the post, anyway), but no provision was made for compression under the post above.

Connector manufacturers' catalogs give the maximum loads that each strap can handle, along with the required number of nails. Still, I have seen many instances where a strap had five or 10 times as many nails as needed. A magazine article showed a steel strap with a capacity of 1,600 pounds, but stated that because they put 150 nails in it, it could resist 15,000 pounds!

3.7.3 Installing tie-downs next to door openings

Although the studs next to doors serve as shear wall end-posts when you have a shear wall there, the presence of a tie-down relates to the shear wall, not the door. Placing tie-downs next to a door serves no purpose unless a shear wall segment ends there. Figure 86 shows a tie-down that serves no structural purpose, but will annoy the door installer.

Figure 85
BAD—Threaded rod provides for tension, but I-joist blocking will
crush under large compression forces. See Figures 66 and 67 for a
proper installation.

3.7.4 Taking extra effort to make panel joints fall away from the sides of window and door openings

This myth comes from an incorrect assumption of what a shear panel alone can do. It began before walls became chopped up with so many window and door openings. Panels do not have enough strength to splice wall segments together around openings. The code specifically prohibits using shear panels to splice joints in this way (SDPWS Section 4.3.6.1).

The section entitled "Openings through Shear Walls" on Page 131 shows the proper way to reinforce shear walls around openings for windows, ducts, electric panels and such. This is done using steel straps and rows of blocks. As an example, Figure 87 shows a vertical strap from the trimmer studs to a header that runs continuously over the return wall. This accomplishes the same thing as the blocking and strapping discussed in the "openings" section, just rotated 90 degrees. This reinforcing principle is used in the connections for Simpson Strongwalls in their "portal" system, and the APA's recently published "Sturd-I-Frames for Narrow Wall Bracing". [15]

Figure 86
The tie-down next to the doorway at right serves no purpose.

Figure 87
Use straps at corners of openings; do not rely on shear panels to reinforce the corners.

3.7.5 Do not nail shear panels to every single stud at multiple end studs

You need to nail shear panels at "edge nail" spacing to shear wall end-posts. However, installing more than one row of edge nailing will actually reduce the overall performance of the shear wall. Figure 88 shows what often occurs at built-up studs at the end of a shear wall (some inspectors actually require this—fight them on this point!). All these nails will make this end of the shear wall much more rigid than the remainder of the wall. As the wall racks back and forth during an earthquake, the rigidity of this connection will overpower the connections in the remainder of the wall, and they will fail first. The CUREE-Caltech Woodframe Project's testing showed that uniform nailing along all panel edges gives the best shear wall performance. There are some exceptions to this generalization, as noted in other sections of this book.

Figure 88
Save those nails for where you really need them! The four extra rows of nails will actually worsen this shear wall's performance.

3.7.6 Building walls with 3x or 4x studs everywhere (you only need thicker studs under panel joints in heavier walls)

Some engineers require 3x or 4x material for all studs at heavier shear walls to be sure you will always land your panel joints over a thicker stud. Using thicker studs for an entire wall run sacrifices money and trees for the sake of expedience. Five or 10 minutes of planning could save you a bundle. Figure 89 shows plenty of wasted lumber.

Figure 89
How to waste 4x studs

3.7.7 Staggering the horizontal joints in tall shear walls

This section has already triggered some debate among engineers. If your plans call for staggered panels, skip this section and stagger away. Figure 90 shows a wall that must have frustrated the framers. While sheathing joints are typically staggered on roof or floor framing, this is usually done to gain strength that is more than made up for in a shear wall by installing blocking behind all the panel edges. Shear walls with staggered panel joints will deform about 25 percent less than walls with all the joints lined up. The less your walls deform, the better. From my experience, though, we need to focus on more basic issues. In this particular building, these issues included tie-downs without nuts on the anchor rods, end-posts without adequate nailing from the shear panels and inadequate panel edge nailing—more than enough problems to offset any benefit from staggering the panel edges. Personally, I feel that the framer's time is better spent in taking extra care while nailing than staggering rows of blocks as shown in Figure 91 to accommodate staggered panel joints. If your designer requires staggered panel joints, recognize that you will be building a superior shear wall—and remember all the other details, too!

Figure 90
Designers: Shear walls are difficult enough to build without staggering the panel joints.

3.7.8 Installing sheathing over an entire wall when only part of it will act as a shear wall segment

Sometimes it saves time to sheath an entire wall even if only part of it will serve as a shear wall. This also provides superior strength and stiffness to the overall building. When desired, though, you can save considerable labor and material by installing shear panels only where the plans call for them. To bring the remaining wall surface out flush with the shear panels, add furring strips to the studs and plates outside the shear wall segment. Figure 92 shows an example of this. Working with narrow strips of sheathing is much easier than using full sheets, and it allows easier access for other trades. Adding furring strips on exterior second-floor walls can be done by reaching out from inside the building, which is much easier than working with whole sheets of sheathing on a scaffold outside.

Figure 91

Inside view of wall shown in Figure 90, showing extra blocking needed for staggered shear panels.

Figure 92

This framer saved money by furring out studs beyond the shear wall end-post rather than fully sheathing the whole wall.

3.7.9 Installing connector hardware for decoration.

The sheet-metal connectors shown in Figure 93 serve absolutely no structural purpose. They follow a chalk line snapped on the outside of the sheathing that corresponds to the bottom of the trusses at the vaulted ceiling inside the house. If someone had cut the panels along the chalk line, then the connectors that span across it would be necessary.

Figure 93

These framing connectors serve no structural purpose at all.

Chapter 4
RELATED TOPICS

FOOTING CONSIDERATIONS

Shear walls may need special footings. For conventional construction, a typical perimeter footing may provide enough strength or weight to resist the uplift forces from a braced wall. However, designers cannot ignore large uplift forces exerted on footings by shear wall tie-downs. A builder should not be expected to know exactly what steps to take to provide for shear wall forces transmitted to the footing. Such decisions are the designer's responsibility, but builders can easily adopt some of the following measures. They should also be aware of footing requirements that may otherwise seem excessive.

4.1.1 Long anchor rods for tie-downs need full embedment in concrete

You may need to deepen footings to provide for longer embedment at anchor rods that will connect to tie-downs. The codes require 3 inches of clearance between embedded steel and the bottom or sides of footing trenches, to allow adequate coverage by the concrete.

4.1.2 Provide top and bottom footing reinforcing bars

Footings for engineered shear walls often need some extra attention. Surprisingly the *Uniform Building Code* only began requiring reinforcement in conventional residential footings in 1997, and then only in the old UBC Seismic Zones 3 and 4, (the former designation for the most active earthquake hazard areas.) Because all concrete cracks as it dries, this leaves unreinforced footings ready to displace under large forces that shear walls can exert on them. You should at least have continuous reinforcing bars along the top and bottom of the footing. In the IBC, footings supporting conventional light frame walls require at least two continuous longitudinal #4 bars. This minimum requirement may not provide nearly enough strength to anchor shear walls in some cases.

Footings at garage return walls often need special reinforcement. Figure 94 shows how a standard footing could fail because of the loading from a shear wall. If your plans call for footing reinforcing that seems excessive, the designer was probably addressing these loads.

4.1.3 Deeper footings resist overturning

Substantial uplift forces at tie-down anchors may require large or deep footings to provide enough dead weight to resist the uplift, as shown in Figure 83. Deciding how large and how deep requires knowing how much friction will develop between the footing and the surrounding soil. Not counting the grip of the surrounding soil (which is usually quite substantial), a $7/_8$-inch anchor rod could easily lift *3 cubic yards* of concrete! Uplift (overturning) forces usually govern the design of footings at shear wall end-posts, even though the downward (compressive) force exerted when lateral forces act in the opposite direction will always combine with the building weight to exceed the uplift. The building designer must state the footing sizes. Stay alert when laying out tie-down anchors though; if you find yourself installing anchors for large tie-downs into forms for a measly little footing pad, give the designer a call.

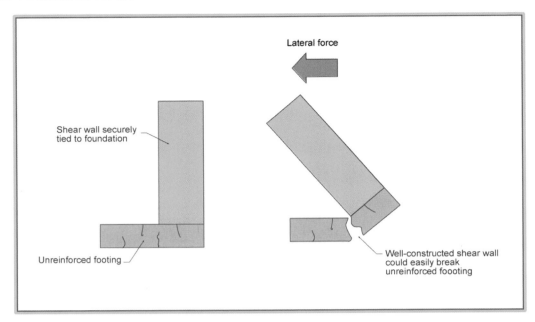

Figure 94
Shear wall can act as lever that can break an unreinforced footing.

4.2

PREFABRICATED SHEAR WALLS AND BRACING PANELS

Several manufacturers make prefab substitutes for site-built shear walls. For their size, these have higher strength than site-built shear walls. Figures 95 and 96 show two examples of prefabricated bracing units.

Figure 95
Simpson Strong-Wall garage portal.

Figure 96
Hardy Frames flanking large windows.

Prefabricated bracing units came about for two main reasons: the need to resist large lateral forces in short lengths of wall and the idea that prefab units would suffer less from installation errors.

Some engineering issues haunt prefab bracing panels. First, some types of bracing units may put the structure into a different design category. Engineers must calculate forces in buildings using braced steel frames, such as Hardy Frames or Z-walls, differently than in buildings with wood-framed shear walls. Second, the narrow panels typically deflect too much to protect building finishes from damage. Manufacturers' literature is full of notes intended to reduce the amount of play in the panel connections. As a panel becomes narrower, it becomes more critical to limit the amount that it can rock up and down, as this movement will be magnified at the top of the panel. Several photos in the following sections show problems that could lead to increased movement of the panel bases.

4.2.1 Engineering and special inspection may be required

The code-approval reports for pre-fab shear walls all state that a registered design professional must provide calculations related to the installation, with some exceptions for products that are approved as a substitute for "braced wall panels." (See Section 1.6.1 for the difference between a prescriptive "braced wall" and an engineered shear wall.) Pre-fab units can place very large loads on building components they attach to. An engineered design must provide for these forces, which often exceed what standard construction could support. The following sections describe some examples where engineering was needed.

For pre-fab shear walls included in an engineered design, the installation will require special inspection during construction. (If the product has approval for replacing braced wall panels and is used in a nonengineered design, special inspection is not required.) Approval reports list the conditions that require special inspection. See IBC Sections 1704.1, 1706 and 1707.

Your local jurisdiction may have other restrictions and conditions regarding pre-fab shear walls. Manufacturers also continue to refine and test their products; check their latest code-approval report for specific requirements.

4.2.2 What's good for the framer may not help the electrician and plumber

Prefab units have strict limits on how many holes you can drill in them for utilities. This can prove extremely frustrating for plumbers and electricians, especially if the units are installed in kitchen or bathroom walls. If you have to furr out around a prefab brace to hide piping and wiring, how much work did you really save? One of the most useful places to use prefab units—for engineers, at least—is next to a garage door. Many localities require photoelectric safety sensors for garage door openers. In this case, the electrician needs to run wiring to the sensor next to the door. If the prefab unit does not allow holes, this can also make what was an easy solution for the designer and framer more difficult overall.

You may be able to turn the prefab unit around to allow for easier wiring. If you need a fixture box on the outside of the wall unit, you can install it with the sheathing toward the inside of the house. Structurally, the unit will serve just as well with the sheathing on the inside or the outside of the wall.

4.2.3 Artificial shear walls do not come with artificial intelligence: Five basic principles still apply to prefab shear walls

Manufacturers have done well in providing templates for anchoring their bracing units to the footing. When used properly, these assure that anchor rods for tie-downs and sill anchor bolts end up in the right place. Some prefab units also come with connectors to fasten them to the main house framing.

Installation errors can make prefab units just as ineffective as a poorly-constructed conventional shear wall. Prefab bracing units really only address one of the five requirements for a shear wall to work: the internal strength of the wall. That still leaves four other ways for prefab units to fail, and an inexperienced plumber or electrician can even compromise the internal strength of a prefab wall panel.

The essential requirements for standard shear walls also apply to prefab units. A brief repetition of these points follows, adapted to prefab units.

Action

A prefab bracing unit does no good unless you connect it properly to the house. The panel shown in Figure 97 should have over a dozen special screws connecting it to the framing above. Figure 98 shows a panel with a manufacturer's stated capacity of 2,865 pounds. The four framing connectors fastening it to the plate above have a combined capacity of only 1,800 pounds—only about two-thirds of what the panel can resist, but still much better than the case in Figure 97.

Reaction

The prefab unit shown in Figure 99 should have proprietary connectors that secure the rectangular steel plate washers to the sill. These connectors apparently were not on hand, so 16-penny nails were used instead. The nails have about 40 percent of the expected connection capacity.

Figure 97
With no connections to the framing above, this shiny bracing panel is useless.

Figure 98
The four framing connectors lack the capacity of this prefab panel.

Figure 99
Hardware supplied by the manufacturer, not ordinary nails, should connect the plate washer to the bottom of this panel.

Figure 100 shows a prefab panel on a second-floor platform. This type of panel is intended for installation only on a slab or concrete curb. (The manufacturer does produce a model for use on platform framing, which requires very specific measures to provide for the reaction and bearing capacity at the panel base.) Figure 101 shows the underside of the floor framing. The $5/8$-inch all-thread rods can transfer the base reaction into nothing more than the plywood subfloor. The installer extended the all-thread down through the double plate to some square plate washers with good intentions, but in this case the important connection point is more than a foot above the washers. This connection falls far short of the panel's intended capacity.

Figure 100
Prefab panels need special provisions when installed on framed floors; Figure 101 shows what supports this panel.

Tie-downs

Compare the huge tie-down brackets attached to the panel end-posts in Figure 100 to the much smaller brackets that connect the anchor rods to the built-up studs below, which are shown in Figure 101. The small brackets would fail long before the prefab unit reached its capacity. Larger brackets could handle the overturning, but there is still not an adequate reaction force.

Figure 101
Framing under prefab panel shown in Figure 100. This installation will not provide reaction force or bearing capacity.

Bearing capacity

For the installation shown in Figures 100 and 101, the rim joist provides the only bearing capacity for the large compressive loads that the prefab panel could exert on the floor framing system. Adding "crush-blocks" in line with the prefab panel end-posts would provide bearing through the floor system; studs must also align under the crush blocks.

The spalled curb shown in Figure 102 will not support the prefab panel end-post installed on it very well. This spalling could also affect the connections that provide the base reaction and overturning resistance of this panel. Some carefully injected epoxy could solve these problems; waiting another day to strip the forms would have been easier.

The small shim under the bracing unit in Figure 103 will not adequately support the end-post. The gap under the post is very small, but a tall, narrow bracing unit will magnify this, allowing the top of the wall to deflect up to six times the gap dimension. This deflection will occur before the unit begins to carry its design lateral load and will greatly reduce the unit's effectiveness in protecting the wall finishes from damage. This type of panel is intended to bear directly on concrete. Any gaps should be shimmed tightly with sheet metal shims that will provide full bearing under the end-post or filled with sand-cement dry-pack.

Providing adequate bearing capacity becomes increasingly important with narrower bracing units. You want the unit to have a rock-solid mounting to the footing. Wet-setting the unit into mortar or epoxy would help it perform. At least one manufacturer has developed a tie-down system for their prefab units that uses the anchor rod to resist both tension and compression, which helps address this concern.

Figure 102
Badly spalled curb will not provide reaction, tie-down force or bearing capacity of undamaged footing.

Figure 103
This shim under corner of prefab wall will not provide adequate support for the bracing panel.

4.3.3 Building collectors from scratch

When you do not have a continuous member, you must assemble one. In the preceding example, connecting a few pieces of plate stock was easy enough. Creating a collector that runs perpendicular to framing members takes greater effort. Figure 109 shows a collector assembled within second-floor framing by installing blocks and a beam tied together with a steel strap.

Figure 109
Strap collects force from blocks and carries it to the shear wall beyond.

For a collector running across the framing members, we want our strap and row of blocks to collect force in the floor diaphragm. This is illustrated in Figure 110. Nails from the diaphragm sheathing into the blocks transfer a small amount of force from the diaphragm into each block. How the force gets from each block to the shear wall depends on the direction in which the force acts, explained as follows.

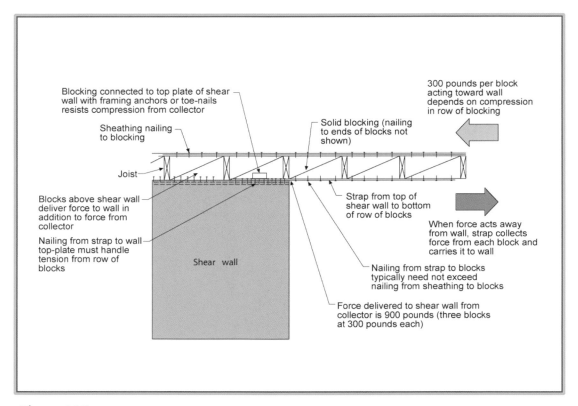

Figure 110
A collector built perpendicular to framing members. In this example, the diaphragm exerts a force of 300 pounds on each block. Note that the framing members could be joists or rafters.

Compression in the collector

If the force in the diaphragm pushes toward the shear wall along the row of blocks (compression force in the collector), we do not need to worry about the steel strap yet. Starting with the block farthest from the shear wall, each block pushes against the next one closer to the wall. The second-farthest block has one other block pushing against it, the next closer block has two blocks pushing against it, and so on. By the time we reach the shear wall, the last block in line pushes against the shear wall with the force collected from the whole row of blocks.

Once we reach the shear wall with our row of blocks, we must transfer the force from the blocks to the wall. The blocking above the shear wall must have sufficient connections (usually framing connectors are needed) to deliver the force collected along the whole row of blocks, including the blocks directly above the wall.

Tension in the collector

When the force we need to collect and transfer to the shear wall acts away from the wall (tension force in the collector), we need to rely on the strap. In Figures 109 and 111, the strap nailed along the bottom of the blocks collects the force from each block and carries it to a shear wall just outside the photo.

More about blocks and straps

Each block must transfer force from the sheathing to the strap. This means that you must use full-depth blocking for straps installed under the framing. In the case of I-joists, this requires blocks cut from engineered lumber (LVL, LSL or PSL).

As a side note, blocks installed with sheathing above and a strap below them act as shear elements. The sheathing applies a force at the top in one direction, and the strap applies an equal force on the bottom of the block in the opposite direction. Remember that a shear element must have a force along each of its four sides to keep it from rotating. The blocks in Figure 111 have gaps between them and the joist webs. In most cases this would not concern me. The blocks are held fairly tightly on three sides and would have a difficult time trying to rotate. But if this was a large collector, the blocks should be toe-nailed to web stiffeners at the joists. This can make using I-joists very labor intensive.

Figure 111
This strap will carry tension force to a nearby shear wall. Ideally, ends of blocks would connect to joists.

We can also nail a strap directly to the sheathing, as shown in Figure 112. For straps installed perpendicular to the framing members, we must install blocks under the sheathing. The blocks will act as backing for the strap nailing, but more importantly they will take the compression forces when the collector acts in compression. As an alternative, you can install the strap first and then the sheathing, as shown in Figure 113. The carpenter routed a $1/8$-inch slot for the strap so it would not create a lump in the sheathing. Note that this requires nailing the strap to the blocking and then the sheathing to the blocking. If the strap was installed on top of the sheathing, the same nails would connect strap, sheathing and blocks.

4.3.4 Remember the load path

Continuous path

Following the load path, the forces we want to collect are in the floor or roof diaphragm. We must nail the sheathing to the collector, whether it is a joist, truss or row of blocks. The collector forms the load path to the shear wall. If the collector member does not fall on the regular framing layout, the sheathing may not get nailed to it at all, and you will have a gap in the load path. Figure 114 shows a strap that will connect to the roof truss that is not on the regular layout. The worker nailing off the sheathing must nail to this truss to complete the load path. The plans should clearly note where to provide additional nailing. When collectors run perpendicular to the framing, it is very easy to overlook nailing the sheathing to the row of blocks unless the strap is on top of the sheathing to remind you. Again, the plans should show these connections.

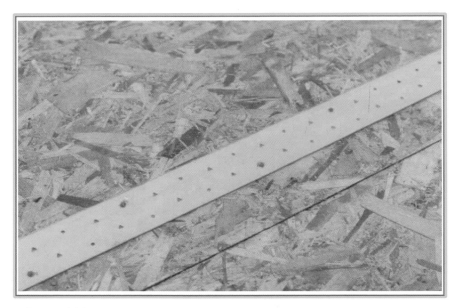

Figure 112
Strap nailed through sheathing to blocking. Holes usually do not all need nails.

Figure 113
Strap installed under floor sheathing will not make a lump under the carpet, but makes for more nailing.

Figure 114
The strap from the shear wall (lower middle of photo) will connect to the off-layout truss; the roof sheathing must also connect to this truss.

Completing the load path to the shear wall requires nailing the strap to the shear wall top plate, as well as providing for transferring compression in the collector to the shear wall top plate. Figures 115 through 117 show how a strap nailed first to the top plate of a wall connects later to the bottom of a collector (in this case a girder truss). The strap will act in tension; eave blocks fitted snugly against the end of the truss and nailed to the top plate will resist the truss pushing against them when the load direction changes. (The eave blocks were not installed at the time the photo was taken.)

The photos do not show the sheathing nailing to the collector (girder) truss. We can probably assume that because the collector truss occurs at the edge of the sheathed diaphragm, the sheathing was nailed to the truss every 6 inches. In the installation shown—and similar cases with a California-framed gable over the main roof—the main roof sheathing must extend all the way to the collector.

Consistent capacity of the load path

Remember that we need to transfer forces from the floor or roof sheathing into the strap and then to the shear wall. Look again at Figure 111. The strap has about 10 nails connecting it to each block. How many nails do you think connect the sheathing to each block? If only three or four nails connect the sheathing to the block, we certainly don't need more than three or four nails from the block to the strap. Too many nails can split wood members, which will defeat the purpose of a collector.

Some inspectors insist that you nail all holes in a strap. If you have a good relationship with the inspector you could explain why straps do not always need complete nailing. Figure 112 shows a strap designed, inspected and approved by a structural engineer. It has just the right number of nails installed to collect the diaphragm forces and deliver them to a shear wall. This strap extends across 40 feet of roof and picks up plenty of force over that length even with nails spaced every 9 inches.

Figure 115

The straps shown above connect to tops of shear walls on either side of the room extension.

Figure 116

Roof sheathing and girder truss are now in place over the opening, ready for final strap connection.

Figure 117

Completed strap installation with straps nailed to the bottom of the collector. Eave blocking must still be installed and connected to shear wall top plate.

4.3.5 Collector Problems

Problems arise most often when framing members run perpendicular to the force we need to collect. The following illustrate some common situations.

Many short straps do not equal one long strap

The line of blocks between the roof trusses shown in Figures 118 and 119 will serve as a collector in compression but will fail miserably in tension. At some point along the line, the collected forces will overwhelm the individual strap connections across each truss. Think of a tug-of-war between two parts of your house. On one team, each teammate would be holding on to a short length of rope held by the next person. Only the person at the front of the line would be holding the rope that the other team is pulling on. That teammate's grip would have to hold the combined force of his whole team. Figure 120 shows this hopeless tug-of-war.

Designers must account for the tension force that a collector carries, and builders must install the components properly or severe damage may result. Problems such as the grossly overloaded collector in Figure 118 can occur when the plans just note "drag-tie" or "block and strap in line with wall." Without adequate detail shown on the drawings, the carpenters made their best guess as to what the designer meant.

Figure 118
Good intentions, but major problems; a single, full-length strap should have been used instead of many separate straps across the bottom chords of these trusses.

Gaps in rows of blocks can lead to failure

In contrast to the collector in Figures 118 and 119, Figure 121 shows a collector that will fail in compression. The gap in the row of blocks will need to close before the collector can deliver any force to the shear wall to the right (outside the photo). This gap will not close gently during an earthquake. While the floor sheathing above will take some level of seismic loads, repeated back and forth movement of the house will cause this gap to close and open many times, slamming the separate building segments against each other with thousands of pounds of force. Furthermore, the strap spanning the gap will buckle and straighten each time the gap closes and opens. After several cycles the strap will fatigue and break, which could allow the gap to open up much more than two inches. The two building segments could then separate completely or just bash each other to bits.

Figure 119
Another view of inadequate straps shown in Figure 118.

Figure 120
Tug-of-war. The team on the left will need really strong hands—and shoulders. Collectors need to form a continuous "rope."

Many commercial buildings collapsed or suffered major damage in the 1994 Northridge earthquake because of this sort of failure. These failures prompted UBC changes that reflect the importance of collectors. When sizing collectors in such buildings, designers must now use an additional safety factor compared to what the code previously required. These changes do not affect buildings with wood-framed shear walls but indicate the importance of collectors to structural safety.

Figure 121
Gap in blocking will allow this collector to fail in compression.

Install straps without kinks or sharp bends

For a steel strap to work effectively it must be installed without sharp bends, kinks or twists. The strap shown in Figure 122 has lost some of its strength because of the twist pounded into it. It will also tend to straighten when put in tension, which in this case could displace the top plate or joist that it connects to, or rip nails out of these members.

Figure 122
The kink in this strap weakens it.

Tricked by a tract—collectors from nowhere

The strap shown in Figure 123 connects to a truss that should have plenty of sheathing nails driven into the top of it. This truss will act as a collector. The strap ties the truss to a shear wall that will transmit the collected forces to the footing. The strap in Figure 125, however, does not connect to anything meaningful. (This shows the same condition as Figure 24, in the "Action" section in the preceding chapter, except the shear wall is shifted to the right.) Correcting this would involve the same procedure used to transmit the action force to the shear wall top plate, namely installing sheathed frames between the trusses, nailing the strap along the entire row of frames and nailing the roof sheathing to the frames.

These photos demonstrate a common problem in tract home construction. The floor plan of the house shown in Figure 124 is identical to the floor plan of the house in Figure 126, but the roof lines were changed from one house to the other in an attempt to disguise the repetitive nature of these houses. Too often, such alternate roof plans are overlooked by the engineer, changed by the architect, altered by the truss manufacturer or revised by the builder. Whatever the cause, the blocks shown will not collect any force during an earthquake, allowing the two segments of the house to separate.

WOOD SHRINKAGE

4.4.1 Effects of wood shrinkage

When lumber dries, it shrinks much more across its width than along its length. (Balloon framing was popular for brick-faced houses for this reason; the full-height studs used would not shrink much relative to the brick.) Most houses built with platform framing will settle about $1/2$ inch per story as the lumber dries out. To most people this may only mean a few drywall cracks, nail pops or floor squeaks. These problems may result in callbacks for the builder, but shrinkage may have much greater implications for shear walls. As framing lumber dries and shrinks, connections to shear wall tie-down hardware become loose. This happens because the anchor rods or strap ties remain the same length as the wood settles down around them.

When to worry

Investigations into existing construction have found nuts on tie-down anchor rods that looked like they had never been tightened. The actual cause was the wood framing shrinking out from under the nuts, bringing the tie-downs along and leaving the nuts loose. Some nuts had as much as a $3/4$-inch gap between them and the tie-down seat (see Figure 127). Testing has shown that slack in a tie-down connection of just $1/4$ inch can reduce a shear wall's capacity by 30 to 40 percent.[16] The top of a shear wall will also move much farther back and forth if its base is not anchored tightly. Remember how much damage to building finishes this deflection can cause.

Code requirements

Section 2303.7 of the IBC requires that "consideration shall be given in design to the possible effect of cross-grain dimensional changes considered vertically which may occur in lumber fabricated in a green condition." The code does not provide any more information. Professionals using the code are expected to know how to address this.

Strap to shear wall beyond

Figure 123
HOUSE "A" interior. Strap from truss bottom chord.

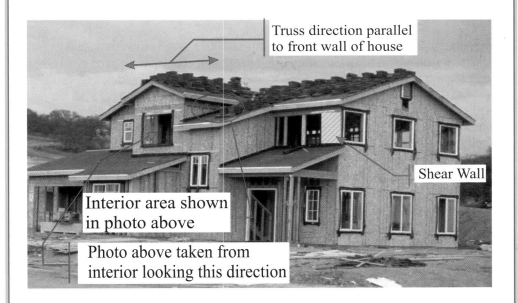

Truss direction parallel to front wall of house

Shear Wall

Interior area shown in photo above

Photo above taken from interior looking this direction

Figure 124
HOUSE "A" exterior. Trusses running in line with shear wall at right serve as collector.

Figure 125
HOUSE "B" interior. Strap does not connect to anything fastened to roof sheathing.

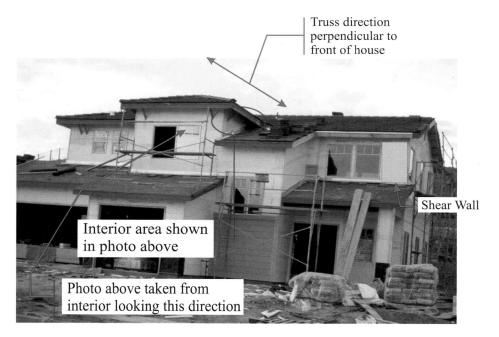

Figure 126
HOUSE "B" exterior. Change in truss direction for hip roof requires different approach to collector.

Until recently most engineers have gone no further than requiring workers to tighten all nuts on bolted connections (which would include shear wall tie-downs) at the latest practicable time before enclosing them with further construction.

Figure 127
This nut was installed snugly—then the wood framing shrunk and settled down about $^3/_4$ inch, leaving the connection loose and very ineffective.

4.4.2 How to compensate for shrinkage

For standard platform construction built at a rapid pace, waiting until "the latest practicable time" to retighten shear wall connections may give the framing less than a month to dry before insulation and drywall go in. For pond-dried lumber in a humid climate or cool building season, most shrinkage will occur after the connections are closed in. In most cases, positive measures should be taken to reduce the effects of shrinkage.

Engineered or kiln-dried lumber

"Engineered lumber" products such as I-joists, parallel strand lumber (PSL—another term for "Parallam" products), laminated strand lumber (LSL) and laminated veneer lumber (LVL) should arrive at your jobsite almost as dry as they will ever get. (Glued-laminated lumber is manufactured at about 15 percent moisture content and will still shrink after installation.) Using I-joists, PSL, LSL and LVL products for floor framing will greatly reduce cross-grain shrinkage compared to, say, 2 x 12 joists. Wall top and bottom plates will still shrink somewhat. Using surface-dry lumber (marked "S-DRY" in the grade-stamp) for top and bottom plates and engineered lumber joists for floor framing could reduce shrinkage to a degree that most engineers would not lose any sleep over.

Kiln-dried (KD) framing lumber would also reduce or eliminate shrinkage problems. Depending on your location, you may find that kiln-dried lumber costs too much to use as a practical alternative. In southern and central California, lumber dries very quickly during the building season by just sitting at the yard or job site. Therefore, most lumberyards do not stock KD lumber in quantities and sizes for a whole lumber package. However, contractors in the Pacific Northwest report that using KD lumber for an entire structural frame is common. The savings in callbacks for drywall repair alone could make the extra expense of KD worthwhile, ignoring the improvement in shear wall performance. If you want kiln-dried pressure-treated sill stock, you must specify "KDAT" (kiln-dried after treatment).

Special hardware

Automatic take-up devices, or "TUDs," that take up the slack in connections are becoming more widespread. After installing one of these devices between the tie-down and the nut, you remove a screw or pin that activates the self-tightening action. Currently, TUDs either rely on ratcheting action or self-tightening threads. One variety of the ratchet-action TUDs can take up 2 inches of shrinkage. A single threaded TUD can take up about 1 inch of slack (see Figure 128); for cases when you expect more than 1 inch of shrinkage you can stack two or more of them on top of each other. Currently costing about $25 each, these could easily double the connection hardware costs for shear walls. This may seem like a lot, but if you go to the trouble to build a shear wall properly in all other respects, you want it to really work when it needs to.

The first Simpson catalog to list take-up devices states that their TUDs "are required for catalog loads" to be achieved when installing their Strong-Wall bracing panels in second-floor locations.

Because of their geometry, short shear wall segments suffer much greater movement than long segments when shrinkage occurs. Designers will need to decide when automatic take-up devices are necessary. I suggest using them anywhere that there will be more than one thickness of non-kiln-dried framing lumber between the footing and bottom of the tie-down post.

If the house has a crawl space that allows sufficient access, you could use turnbuckles to connect anchor rods from shear walls above to the footing anchors. You will probably not find turnbuckles at your lumberyard; try a welding or steel fabricating shop. You will also need a length of rod with left-hand threads on one end and right-hand threads on the other (usually supplied with the turnbuckle). Turnbuckles will help only if someone actually tightens them periodically during the first year or so after construction, until the house framing has stopped shrinking; using hardware specifically designed for the purpose is probably much more practical.

See Appendix A for another possibility regarding shrinkage compensation.

Figure 128
Automatic take-up device (TUD).

Wait for construction to dry out

Waiting for your framing to air-dry may work in the Southwest, and then probably only in summer for moderately paced construction. A good moisture meter would cost less than a house worth of automatic take-up devices described above. Equilibrium moisture content (when the wood stops shrinking) for dry climates is in the range of 4 to 7 percent. If you read less than eight to 10-percent moisture in your framing, you could probably close in your tie-down connections and not worry that they would loosen appreciably because of shrinkage. If you build during the rainy season or in a moist climate, take-up devices will cost much less than delaying construction while waiting for your lumber to dry out.

Chapter 5

ADVANCED SHEAR WALLS

OPENINGS THROUGH SHEAR WALLS

Engineers love long, uninterrupted, solid shear walls. Instead we get walls with windows, doors, fireplace openings, window bays and HVAC penetrations (see Figures 129 and 130). Usually we can create enough shear wall length between such obstructions to meet the design requirements. In some cases, we cannot avoid cutting an opening through a shear wall. Or sometimes what we designed as a solid wall later has a duct opening or a whim window cut into it.

Going back to the section that discusses shear elements, we realize that we have a problem. If we draw a square on our shear wall, each edge of the square has the same force acting along it. What can provide this force if we cut out and remove an adjacent square of paneling? Nothing but air (or window glass). Reinforcing at openings in shear walls evens out the shear forces around the opening.

Figure 129
Engineer's dream wall.

Figure 130
Architect's dream wall.

5.1.1 Blocking and strapping reinforces around openings

Figure 131 shows how to reinforce above and below an opening in a shear wall. The blocking and strapping in line with the header will collect horizontal force from the shear panels above the opening and distribute the force to panels on both sides of the opening. If the lateral force at the top of the wall acts from right to left, then the blocks on the left side of the header are in compression. At this moment the strap on the left side of the header carries no load. The opposite is true on the right side of the header: The strap carries tension, but the blocks do nothing until the load at the top of the wall reverses direction. The blocks, header and strap form a collector within the shear wall. The force that it collects equals the force per foot in the wall above the opening times the width of the opening.

Now the total action force has been transferred into the wall segments on either side of the opening. Another collector, this time composed of the window sill and blocks and straps in line with it, redistributes the action force out across the full width of the wall below the opening.

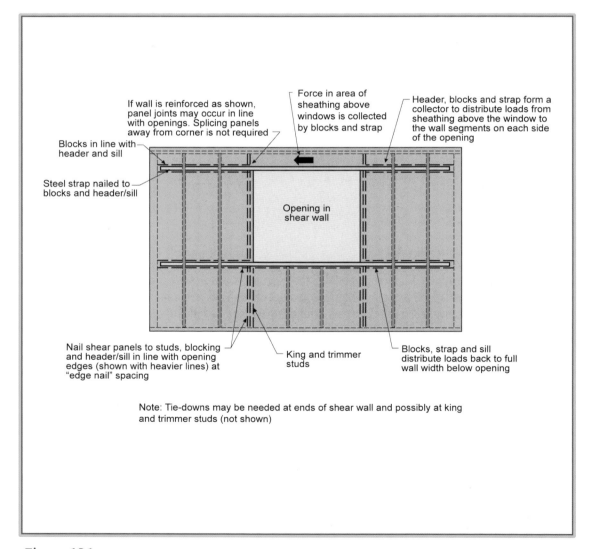

Figure 131

Reinforce around openings in shear walls with continuous elements that extend out from all edges of the opening. In this case, the vertical elements are the king and trimmer studs; the horizontal elements are the sill, header, rows of blocks and continuous straps.

The sheathing and straps must be nailed at the "edge nail" spacing for the particular shear wall you are building. You may install the straps over the shear panels or place them on the opposite side of the wall and nail them to the blocks. Installing straps over the panels will save nailing, as the same nails serve to connect the sheathing to the blocks and the strap to the sheathing. It should be noted again that too many nails in one area of sheathing will cause areas with fewer nails to fail prematurely. If you need to nail a strap over sheathing, do not nail the sheathing to the framing before installing the strap. The nails from the strap will also connect the sheathing. (Note: the preceding may seem to contradict the advice given in "Above and beyond the code" on Page 93 that advises connecting strap-type tie-downs directly to the end-posts. In the case of a tie-down, force from the strap needs to transfer to the shear wall end-post. Transferring this force through a layer of sheathing increases the deflection of the system. In the case of a strap applied on top of sheathing to reinforce around an opening, the force in the strap only has to transfer to the sheathing, and not an element behind it; therefore the strap is just as effective on top of the sheathing.)

To keep the strap out of the way of drywall, you may wish to install it before the shear panels. First, recess the blocks (install them flatwise) and rout a $1/_8$-inch-deep slot in the studs, sill and header. This will eliminate a bulge under the drywall, but still leave the trim carpenters wondering why all their nails keep bending near the window. It isn't much consolation, but engineers don't like designing this any more than carpenters like building it.

The wall next to the window opening in Figure 132 has full-length rows of blocks, but the straps should also extend to the end of the wall. Full-length straps (collector elements) are required by SDPWS Section 4.3.5.2, Item 4.

Figure 132
HALF-BAD—Blocks extend full length of wall in line with window header and sill; so should the straps.

5.1.2 Nail to studs on both sides of the opening with edge nail spacing along the full stud height

The studs on either side of the opening must also serve as collectors. Because they are continuous elements, they can provide tension or compression forces, whereas in the horizontal direction we needed blocks for the compression and straps for the tension forces. We simply need to nail the sheathing to these studs at the required edge nail spacing.

The effect of the preceding steps is to make a three-level shear wall. Above the opening you have a long, uninterrupted shear wall connected to a continuous member made up of the blocking and strapping at the header level. On either side of the opening you have two narrow shear wall segments connected to the same continuous element above. The base of these narrow segments attaches to the top of another uninterrupted width of shear wall below. The king and trimmer studs next to the opening provide the tie-down forces for the inside edges of the narrow shear wall segments. Note that the king and trimmer studs often require tie-downs, in addition to the tie-downs at the ends of the wall. Occasionally, blocking and strapping around an opening can eliminate the need for tie-downs at the studs next to the opening.

PERFORATED SHEAR WALLS

The UBC included two types of shear wall design methods. The traditional method used full height shear wall segments that comply with height and width requirements that were usually restrained against overturning by tie-down devices at both ends of each wall segment. The second method considered the entire shear wall with openings; the forces around the perimeter of the openings are analyzed, designed and detailed as described above. The IBC (as referenced in the SDPWS) allows these two shear wall design methods plus a third method called the "perforated shear wall." This is an empirical approach based on research done in Japan and at Virginia Tech. This method does not require tie-downs adjacent to openings, and no reinforcement around openings is required. The code imposes a lot of limitations and specific design requirements for perforated shear walls, and they must be designed by licensed professionals. Most of the principles presented in this book still apply to perforated shear walls, save the requirements for tie-downs at both ends of each wall segment (you still may need tie-downs at both ends of the whole wall).

SHEAR WALLS WITH SLOPING TOPS

The APA tested horizontal plywood and structural panel diaphragms in addition to shear walls. The results of those tests form the basis for most floor and roof diaphragm design. The tables presented in the building codes for diaphragm design clearly state, "for horizontal . . . diaphragms." How do engineers justify using these tables to design sloping diaphragms for the typical residential roof? By invoking the reasoning that we hate to hear contractors use: "We've always done it that way." The APA[17] presents fair justification for this, and most engineers and plan checkers have no problems applying the horizontal capacities from the diaphragm design tables to sloped diaphragms. However, I have not seen any literature address how shear walls act when connected to those sloping diaphragms. The following section presents an overview of shear walls with sloped top plates. For engineers who wish to study this further, Appendix B presents an analysis of the subject. The approach is slightly different than the method typically used in the past to design sloping shear walls but more accurately reflects the physical principles involved.

5.3.1 Additional vertical force occurs at low end of wall

In residential construction, shear walls with sloping top chords occur at gable end walls as shown in Figures 17 and 133, and interior walls parallel to the gable end as shown in Figure 18.

Figure 133
Shear wall segments with sloped top plates require special connections.

When a shear wall with a sloped top plate receives an "action force", that force acts along the sloping plate. The action forces we have considered in our examples so far were applied horizontally. How do we deal with a sloping force? Engineers would analyze the sloping force as two components: one acting horizontally and the other vertically (see Figure 134). This means that part of our top-plate force acts in the vertical direction (whether it acts up or down depends on the direction of the action force). Our shear wall can transfer the horizontal force component to the footing in the typical way. However, the post at the short end of the shear wall must handle the added vertical force component in addition to the typical end-post force. Furthermore, when the vertical force component acts upward we must keep the sloped top plate from lifting up.

5.3.2 Provide additional uplift capacity at the short end-post

To keep the sloped rafter or top plate from lifting up we need to install a strap from it to the short shear wall end-post. To transfer the additional force to the footing, we also need a stronger tie-down at the short end-post than at the tall end-post.

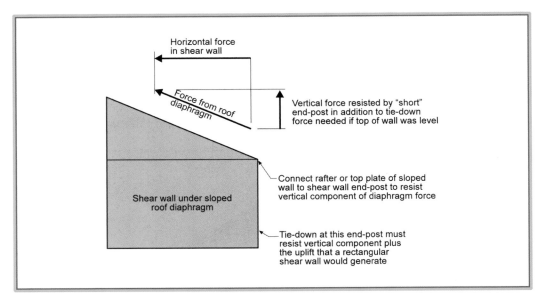

Figure 134
Action force broken down into horizontal and vertical components. The vertical component quickly becomes significant for roof slopes over 2:12.

Figure 135 shows a strap intended to handle the upward force from the sloping top plate of a retrofit shear wall. (Because this wall was sheathed after the roofing was installed, framing connectors and $1/2$-inch wafer-head screws were used to connect to the underside of the roof sheathing.) The photo shows the upper portion of the wall shown in Figures 63 and 64, which explains why the strap is so far away from the end of the wall. (And no, that is not A/C plywood at $40 per sheet—it's Structural 1 grade, at about 15 percent more than C/D.)

Figure 135
This strap ties the sloped top plate of this interior retrofit shear wall to the tie-down post.

5.3.3 Further study needed

I am not aware that anyone has studied the mechanics of what happens to a sloped shear wall. The next section discusses why shear walls with sloped **bottoms** should be avoided; what can we do about shear walls with sloping tops? Should we worry about them? The following factors warrant consideration:

- How steep is the slope? The effects discussed above get more and more severe as the slope increases.

- How many other shear walls are in the building? If only a few shear walls resist wind and seismic forces, each wall needs to be as strong as possible.

STEPPED FOOTINGS AND HILLSIDE ANCHORS

5.4.1 Shear wall segments should not vary in height along a wall

When footings and stemwalls step down a hillside, shear walls built to follow the steps will not function well together to resist lateral forces. Figure 136 shows a stepped footing with cripple shear wall segments. (Older homes built on slopes sometimes had footings with sloping tops rather than steps; this discussion also applies to shear walls that might be built on top of sloping footings.) The rim joist and footing will grip the top and bottom of each segment. When lateral forces act on the rim joist it will shift the top of each shear wall segment the same distance. (The same thing occurs in a typical shear wall, but all the panels in a typical shear wall have equal heights.) The short wall segment will rack much more than the taller segments for the same movement of the rim joist. Figure 137 shows how the shortest cripple wall segment will fail first, followed by the next tallest segment, succeeding down the steps. Movement of the rim joist in the opposite direction will mash the shear wall segments against the tops of the adjacent footing steps, causing the panels further damage.

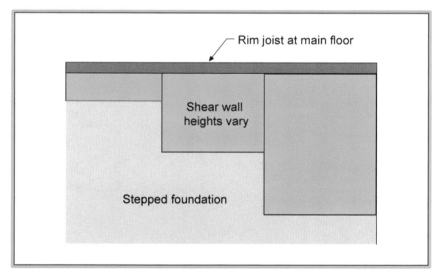

Figure 136
This common hillside construction below main-floor level performs poorly in earthquakes.

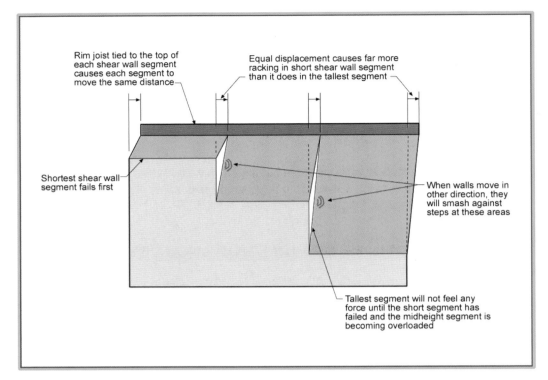

Figure 137
Shear wall segments of different heights along the same wall do not perform well.

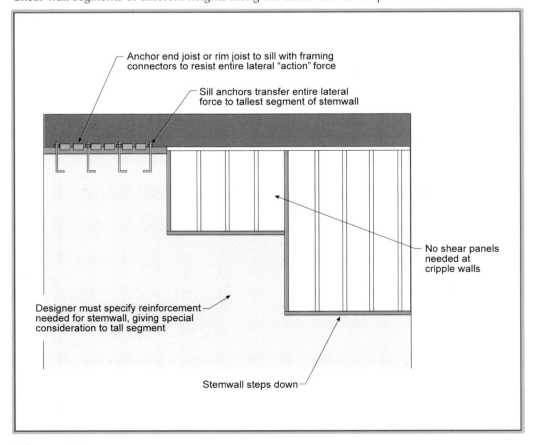

Figure 138
Concentrate the connections at the tallest segment of stemwall, and you do not need any shear panels on the stepped cripple walls.

One possible reason that sloping or stepped cripple walls perform so much worse than shear walls with sloping top plates discussed in Section 5.3 is the rigidity of the footing compared to the roof. The roof diaphragm will flex much more than a footing; this would be more forgiving to the shear wall. Another factor could be the amount of force generated at the roof level versus the floor level; a cripple wall has to resist the total force accumulated at all the levels above, whereas the forces are less just below the roof.

5.4.2 The hillside anchor

One solution to the problem posed by stepped footings is to anchor the rim joist to the highest footing step (in the case shown in Fig 137, this would require raising the left-most stemwall). Fig 138 shows how this change would look.

Another solution is to connect the rim joist to the foundation with a tie-down bracket installed horizontally. The "hillside primary anchor," as this type of connection is called, is already required in the City of Los Angeles. IRC Section R602.11.3 requires a similar approach for stepped footings in Seismic Design Categories D1 and D2 if the braced cripple wall height varies more than four feet. The photos in Figures 139 and 140 show a variation of this, where the end beam of a garage butts into a concrete retaining wall and tie-back system. The left end-post of the "floating" shear wall in Figure 139 is next to the door; the tie-down for it anchors to the underside of a floor beam. The horizontal tie from this beam to the footing is similar to the connection shown in Figure 140.

Figure 139
This shear wall connects to the end beam of the floor framing, which in turn connects to the footing on the left side of the building.

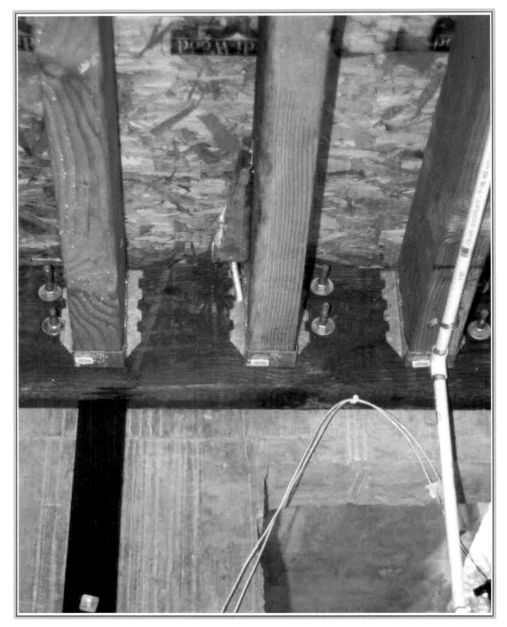

Figure 140
The tie-down bracket connected to the floor beam in the center of the photo connects the building to the hillside footings. (This anchor is on the far end of the building shown in Figure 139).

Chapter 6

EARTHQUAKE RETROFITS FOR CRIPPLE WALLS AND RAISED FLOORS

INTRODUCTION

This chapter presents retrofit methods for wood-framed buildings in areas where earthquakes are known to occur. Areas with earthquake hazards include almost all of the west coast of the U.S. including Alaska; the Hawaiian Islands from Molokai east; Puerto Rico; the New Madrid fault zone (western Tennessee and Kentucky, eastern Arkansas and Missouri, and southern Illinois); the Yellowstone area; the Salt Lake area; and the Charleston, SC area. For more specific information consult an agency like the U.S. Geological Survey. Be aware that building officials in many of these areas were not alive when the most recent local earthquake occurred and may downplay the threat of future quakes; if the *International Building Code* considers your building Seismic Design Category C, D or E, you live in "earthquake country".

At the time of this writing the author believes the following methods to be practical, effective, and economical. Methods presented are based on engineers' observations of damage caused by past earthquakes, experienced contractors' observations of retrofit techniques during installations, results of government-funded testing programs, and independent home inspectors' observations of previously installed retrofits. Any specific house can behave differently in an earthquake than observations from prior earthquakes would indicate. No retrofit installation can make a building "earthquake-proof." Even properly retrofitted buildings may experience severe damage in a large earthquake—but almost certainly less damage than if they had not been retrofitted. The intent of retrofit methods presented in this chapter is to prevent damage that is known to occur in nonretrofitted houses during reasonably foreseeable earthquakes, and only at what has been shown in past earthquakes to be the weakest part of older wood-framed construction: the connections between the foundation and the first floor framing. For older buildings built over crawl spaces, the cripple walls are usually the weakest part of the structure, but they are probably not the *only* weakness.

Substantial structural damage can also occur in houses that do not have cripple walls, or in other portions of houses whose cripple walls have been retrofitted. Vulnerable construction may include attached porches, stairs and balconies; split-level homes; large openings in walls ("soft" or "weak" stories); brick, stone or other heavy veneer on walls; chimneys; and post-and-pier foundations, to name a few. For further information, see FEMA G225, "*Seismic Retrofit Training for Building Contractors and Inspectors*" available from the Federal Emergency Management Agency (FEMA). This chapter is no substitute for the project-specific advice of a competent design professional with experience in wood-framed construction and retrofit work.

This chapter also does not address hazards from nonstructural elements such as: falling water heaters; gas leaks; and falling objects inside the house, such as tall furniture or heavy objects on shelves or inside cabinets. Furthermore, even in the most securely retrofitted building substantial losses can result from damage to the contents of the building. Broken or fallen scattered items can also result in hazards from broken glass, tripping or slipping, etc. For more information on reducing nonstructural hazards, see FEMA 74, *"Earthquake Hazard Mitigation for Nonstructural Elements"* and *"Homeowner's Guide to Earthquake Safety"* by the California Seismic Safety Commission.

This chapter is not meant as a substitute for existing retrofit codes or guidelines, but merely a supplement to them. Several cities along the west coast have generated retrofit programs, including the "Project Impact" program in Seattle, WA; *"Standard Plan A"* (see Reference 20—this was originally developed by the City of San Leandro, CA, and is currently being expanded and refined by other cities in the region); and Los Angeles Department of Building and Safety's *"Earthquake Hazard Reduction in Existing Wood Frame Residential Buildings with Weak Cripple Walls and Unbolted Sill Plates."* The ICC also publishes the *"International Existing Building Code"* (IEBC), of which Chapter A3 contains details for some of the conditions described in this chapter. Additional resources include ATC 50-1, *"Seismic Rehabilitation Guidelines for Detached, Single-family, Wood-frame Buildings"* (Applied Technology Council, Redwood City, CA) and *"Homeowner's Guide to Earthquake Safety"* by the California Seismic Safety Commission.

Lastly, retrofit work is dangerous. Among other concerns, hazards may include the following: dust (including asbestos, depending on existing conditions); insect, snake and spider bites; possible exposure to hazardous chemicals in pest-control treatments or existing or new treated wood; and all hazards related to construction, working in cramped spaces, and the use of hand and power tools. It is the responsibility of the person installing an earthquake retrofit to follow safe practices during all phases of construction, from initial investigation through final inspection and approval.

DISCLAIMER:

Neither the author nor the publisher shall be responsible for any property loss or injury alleged to have occurred due to the use or misuse of any of the following material, nor for injuries sustained in the course of any retrofit work, nor for any other damages related to earthquakes or construction.

ACKNOWLEDGMENTS

This chapter addresses the very basic requirements for retrofitting existing cripple walls in wood-framed buildings to resist earthquakes. The information presented is very limited—this topic warrants a whole book of its own, which is under development. Many thanks to the following reviewers and contributors:

Bay Area Retrofit, Inc, Berkeley, CA

Al Commins; Commins Mfg, Friday Harbor, WA

Kevin Darville; Builder, Vacaville, CA

LaDawn Haws, PhD; California State University, Chico, CA

Fred Lustenberger, Chief Building Official, Town of Tiburon, CA

Neil Moore, SE, SECB, Shingle Springs, California

Jeanne Perkins; Consultant to the Association of Bay Area Governments

Susan Piper, Policy Analyst, City of Oakland, CA

Roger Robinson; Star Inspection Group, Berkeley, CA

Nels Roselund, SE; The Roselund Engineering Co, Rosemead, CA

This chapter obviously cannot address every type of home and is not a substitute for a design provided by a competent design professional or seismic retrofit specialty contractor. The following is intended to give building owners and contractors an overview of which retrofit components are most effective and necessary and which ones border on useless.

Earthquake retrofits are typically not intended to prevent all damage, but rather to keep your home in habitable condition after an earthquake of reasonably predictable magnitude. The Association of Bay Area Governments (ABAG) estimates that the next earthquake on the Hayward Fault will render 155,000 housing units uninhabitable. This disaster will be much more devastating than Hurricane Katrina yet is almost entirely preventable.

6.1

TYPICAL EARTHQUAKE DAMAGE

Older homes suffer the most damage in earthquakes because they either slide off their foundations or the "cripple walls" (short wood-framed walls that support the first floor of the house above the foundation) fail and fall over.

Some houses do not have cripple walls—the first floor framing bears directly on the concrete footing stemwalls. Inadequate anchorage of such a house can result in it sliding off its footings as shown in Figure 141.

Figure 141
The Loma Prieta Earthquake threw this house to the left and off its footings, resulting in severe damage. (FEMA photo by JK Nakata)

Failing cripple walls can result in your house falling several feet. Figure142 shows a house that suffered such a fate.

Figure 142

The Northridge Earthquake shook this house to the right and rear, causing the cripple-walls to collapse. The falling house completely destroyed itself.

(FEMA photo by Andrea Booher)

Keeping your house on its foundation could make the difference between you staying in your home after an earthquake or having to live in a tent or a shelter for an extended time. It could save your house from having to be demolished and rebuilt. Even if you retrofit your home, though, a major earthquake may still damage it—but it is less likely to be *destroyed*.

Houses built before 1950 or so are unlikely to have adequate connections to their footings. To be safe, if your house was built before about 1960, it would be worth checking to see if it is connected to the footings.

ESSENTIAL PARTS OF A RETROFIT

Section 2.2 describes the five essential traits of *new* shear walls. For a seismic retrofit, one has to balance the risk, cost of installation, and an acceptable amount of damage. General consensus among those who study earthquake damage is that following the first three principles listed in Section 2.2 will keep your house from sliding or falling off its foundation during an earthquake. These principles are the "Action", "Reaction", and "Internal Strength" properties of a shear wall. Next we address how a retrofit meets these general requirements. Figures 143A through D show typical methods for retrofitting a cripple wall.

Figure 143A

Unreinforced cripple wall. The worker is installing shear transfer ties to deliver earthquake force from the floor framing to the top of the cripple wall. (This particular sort of connector should only be used if there is solid blocking between the joists to prevent them from rolling.)

Figure 143B

Shear transfer ties connecting the end joist to a reinforced cripple-wall. Until very recently (1994) end joists were typically connected to the top plate with just a few toe-nails as might have been needed to hold it in place during construction.

Figure 143C

Bottom corner of reinforced cripple-wall. Ventilation hole also provides for inspection of mud-sill anchor, as is visible in this photo. Note that the original mudsill was wider than the cripple studs. The original concrete was chipped away to allow removal of excess sill material after it was cut flush with the face of the studs (see Section 6.2.4.1).

Figure 143D

Where floor framing bears directly on the mudsill, specially manufactured brackets like the shiny one at the left provide about the same anchorage as a new 5/8-inch sill bolt. Note that the angle iron on the right in this photo was installed with a wood spacer between it and the concrete, which makes it useless in resisting side-to-side force (angle-iron brackets are often installed poorly, as described in Section 6.4.4).

Typical cripple-wall and crawlspace conditions.

6.2.1 ACTION—Shear transfer ties connect the floor to the top of the cripple wall or to the mudsill

In older homes, the floor that you walk on is often not adequately connected to the building components below it. The floor framing must connect securely to the top of the cripple wall below, or in the case where there is no cripple wall, to the foundation sill ("mudsill").

Commonly used shear transfer ties include metal framing connectors such as Simpson's "L90", USP's "AC9" or KC Metals' "CA90". The connectors fasten the rim joist or blocking in the first floor platform to the mudsill, or to the cripple wall top plate if a cripple wall is present. References such as the IEBC give recommendations on how many framing anchors to install based on various factors such as how many stories are above the cripple wall.

Shear transfer ties almost always have to be installed where it is impossible to swing a hammer (See Figure 143B)." Contractors who do this work will have a pneumatic "palm nailer" that fits into tight spaces and makes short work of nailing these connections.

6.2.2 REACTION—Mudsill connections transfer earthquake forces to the footings.

If your house is not anchored sufficiently to its footings you will need to add more anchors. Retrofit techniques depend mostly on how much headroom you have to work in. Different methods include the following.

6.2.2.1 Moderate to tall crawlspaces allow easier anchor installation

For cripple walls with studs tall enough to allow drilling straight down through the mudsill into the footing, you can connect the mudsill to the footing using drop-in (expansion) anchors, adhesive anchors, or anchors with self-cutting threads.

First locate where you will install the anchors. Next, bore through the mudsill with a wood-boring bit that is $1/16$-inch larger than the anchor diameter. Once you have drilled through the mudsill you can drill into the concrete as needed to set the particular kind of anchor you select. Generally, cripple-studs must be at least 30 inches tall for a typical rotary hammer to fit into a stud space and begin drilling a hole straight down into the concrete footing. Installation requirements for the various sorts of anchors vary and are usually described in detail in manufacturers' literature.

Using toothed washers such as KC Metals' "MSP" (see Section 3.3.14) on top of the sill at anchor bolts will increase the capacity of the connection by about 40 percent. This is a very good return on the 50 cents or so that these washers cost.

6.2.2.2 Low-clearance crawlspaces require special-purpose brackets to anchor mudsills

If you have short cripple walls, or the floor framing rests directly on the mudsill, you will need to use a connector plate that you bolt to the footing and fasten to the mudsill, such as Simpson Strong-Tie's "UFP10" or KC Metals' "RFA138." These brackets attach to the face of the concrete footing and to the top or inside edge of the mudsill, as shown on the left-hand side of Figure 143D. Note that only a few of the connectors shown for footing applications in hardware manufacturers' catalogs are actually designed for the "reaction" force—that is, a sliding force. Section 6.4.3 discusses this in more detail. Note also that with specialized brackets now available, use of "home-made" hardware is unnecessary, untested and possibly harmful (see Section 6.4.4).

6.2.2.3 Install anchors from outside the building through foundation vents

In some cases you can install sill anchors through foundation vent openings. Many homes built in the 1940s and 1950s were built with framing resting directly on the mudsill. Homes built in this period usually have foundation vents spaced eight to twelve feet apart. Members of the Structural Engineers Association of Southern California developed a special bracket that attaches to the mudsill and then provides guidance as you drill holes for the mudsill anchors. The brackets can be placed by removing foundation vent screens, which are replaced after the anchor installation. Each bracket has holes for two anchors; this provides an effective anchor spacing of four to six feet for typical vent spacing. Some work will generally need to be done inside the crawlspace, but most people would rather do as much as possible from the outside.

6.2.3 INTERNAL STRENGTH—Shear panels strengthen the cripple wall

Plywood or OSB gives much greater strength to a cripple wall than common exterior finishes such as stucco or horizontal wood siding. Install the panels as described in Section 3.4. *For best results use $^{15}/_{32}$-inch thick, five-ply plywood.*

Note that an inspector may need to observe new connections from the mudsill to the footing. Installing shear panels on exterior walls will conceal any new anchors you have installed. Depending on the inspector's requirements, you may need to call for an inspection before shear panels obscure new anchors. Some inspectors allow you to provide small access holes through the shear panels near each bolt, so that the anchors can be inspected after the panels are in place; this saves a trip for the inspector. Obviously, you will have to make direct connections through the mudsill to the concrete before installing the shear panels.

Provide ventilation holes near the top and bottom of each stud bay in cases where installing shear panels would create an enclosed space. Required sizes of holes vary depending on local regulations; $2^{1}/_{2}$ to 3 inch diameter holes are typical. The holes should be located with their edges at least an inch above or below the mudsill or top plate, respectively. If located properly they can also provide for visual inspection of the sill anchors. Some jurisdictions require covering the holes with wire mesh.

For installations in areas subject to flooding, check for local regulations that may require "flood vents" that will prevent water pressure from building up on one side of a wall. In such areas you must not install plywood that will create an enclosed, unvented space. Other requirements may include the use of pressure-treated lumber and plywood, and hot-dipped galvanized nails.

Codes such as the IEBC provide for minimum length of new cripple wall sheathing, plywood thickness and nailing schedule, and maximum allowable cripple wall heights.

6.2.4 Cases where the existing mudsill is wider than cripple wall studs

In many older buildings the cripple wall studs are 2 x 4s set on a 2 x 6 mudsill. In this case, the shear panels cannot be installed on the inside face of the cripple wall because the face of the mudsill is not flush with the face of the studs. There are three ways to address this problem, as follows.

6.2.4.1 Flush cutting the mudsill gives the best performance

Special saws allow workers to cut the existing mudsill flush with the face of the studs, as shown in Figure 143C. [As of 2011, the following three companies make flush-cutting circular saws: Cuzdey Manufacturing Technologies (http://www.straightflushsaw.com, Phone 360-591-2046); Clemenson Enterprises, Inc (10650 County Rd. 81, Suite F, Maple Grove, MN 55369, www.cei-clem.com); and Crain Tools (1155 Wrigley Way, Milpitas, CA 95035, www.craintools.com).]

Sometimes the mudsill was set into the wet concrete when the footings were poured, so part or all of the sill is below the top of the stemwall. In this case you may need to break a narrow strip of concrete away to provide nailing access to the face of the mudsill. An air-chisel (commonly used in auto-body work) performs this task well.

The wood you will typically find in an old mudsill is dense, close-grained redwood, and the lumber is usually a full 2 inches thick. This material resists splitting very well when shear panels are nailed to it.

Some retrofit experts argue that the original wider mudsill helped spread the building weight over the width of the footing, and that cutting it off flush with the wall will increase the tendency of footings to roll over in soft soil. Though well intentioned, this concern has little basis in engineering principles. "Footing rotation" does indeed occur fairly often in old, shallow footings that are not centered under the cripple walls, but a wood mudsill and its relatively weak connections to the cripple-wall framing cannot prevent this occurrence. The biggest concern when using the flush-cut method is accounting for the reduced width of the mudsill when installing new mudsill anchors.

The flush-cut mudsill method most closely matches the construction of shear walls as tested over the decades by APA-The Engineered Wood Association and many other groups.

6.2.4.2 "Reverse block" method

For the reverse-block method, you attach a length of lumber (the "reverse block," which may be several feet long) to the shear panel before installing the shear panels to the studs. The panels are nailed from the back into the reverse block. After installing the panels with the pre-attached block, the block is nailed to the existing mudsill. Figure 144 shows the reverse-block method. You may have to notch the reverse block or shear panels to fit around existing mudsill anchors. Your house is much stronger with slightly-notched shear panels than it was without any shear panels.

6.2.4.3 Blocking nailed between studs—the last choice

Nailing blocks to the mudsill between the cripple studs so that the blocks are flush with the studs gives you an even surface to attach the shear panels. This method was developed to allow homeowners to retrofit their own houses, as it is relatively simple and unlike the flush-cut method, does not require special tools. However there are several problems with this method.

First, nailing the blocks to the mudsill often splits the blocks. Split blocks have almost zero connection capacity. Even if you check the blocks and see no splitting before you install the shear panels, you are not finished driving nails into the blocks. All the panel edge nailing into the blocks could cause splitting—and you will not have a way to inspect the blocks once the panels are in place unless the opposite side of the wall is open and accessible.

Splitting issues can be greatly reduced by attaching the blocks with pneumatically-driven staples or with self-drilling structural screws such as Simpson's "SDS" series, USP's "WS" series, or Fasten Master's "Trusslok" series (screw attachment could also reduce the chance of the blocks lifting off the mudsill, as discussed shortly.) Pre-drilling for nails could also prevent splitting, but it is unlikely that anyone besides a very conscientious person would actually pre-drill. "Engineered lumber" such as "Parallam" stock might be less likely to split. Other engineered materials such as LVL or LSL might tend to split or delaminate when plywood nails are driven into the narrow face.

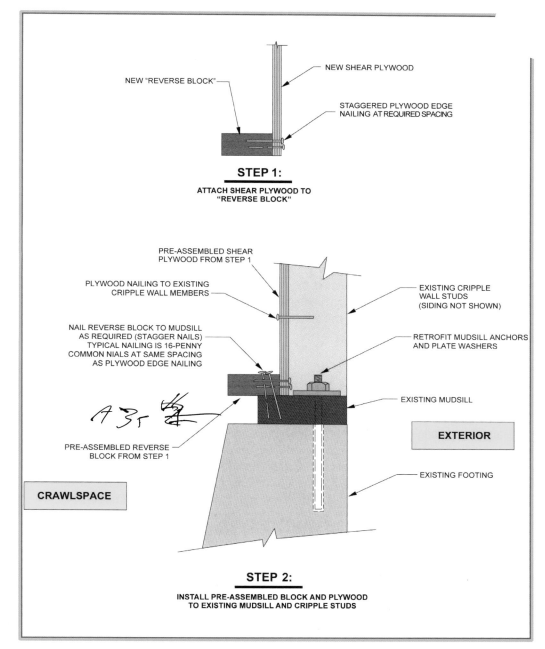

Figure 144
The 'reverse-block' method for connecting shear panels to the mudsill when it is wider than the cripple studs

The second problem with nailed blocks is the increased labor over the methods discussed previously.

Third, nailed blocks lifted off of the mudsill during simulated earthquake loading. CUREE (Reference 21) performed tests on cripple-walls braced using the nailed-block method. Further research is needed, but the tests indicate that installing tie-downs at the ends of braced cripple-walls that use nailed blocks might help them perform better.

In Section 3.3.2 we learned that oversize washers on mudsill anchors are helpful to keep the mudsill from splitting as the shear panels pull up on it. Blocks between studs, as typically installed, have little capacity to resist this uplift. (Tie-downs could help prevent this problem, but a thorough discussion of retrofit tie-downs is beyond the scope of this chapter.) Furthermore, securing the blocks to the mudsill or foundation could cause them to split when shear panels place an upward force on them.

Of several reviewers and contributors asked specifically about the nailed-block method, none of them recommend it over the flush-cut method. This includes the CUREE researchers who performed the tests in Reference 21. The general consensus among retrofit experts is that the nailed-block method should be reserved for cases where neither of the other methods can be used.

Few conditions warrant using the mudsill-block method. One such case is where the existing mudsill was embedded into the concrete and set below the top of the footing. If there are obstructions that prevent chipping away the concrete to allow using the flush-cut or reverse-block method then mudsill blocks may be the best option. Use new foundation anchors that secure the blocks to the footing, install tie-downs when feasible, and use nails only as a last resort to attach the blocks to the existing mudsill.

6.3

Retrofit Priorities

Those who wish to retrofit a building need to know where to start in order to make the most effective use of their budget. In general, home inspectors and engineers find that the older the house the more retrofit work and repairs it will need. The following list briefly addresses some typical cases, beginning with the most important retrofit recommendations as they apply to a typical house. Remember—*your house may not be typical!* Other retrofit measures found in references listed at the beginning of this chapter could have higher priority than the items listed below.

SEE THE INTRODUCTION AT THE BEGINNING OF THIS CHAPTER FOR DISCLAIMER, LIMITATIONS AND OTHER SOURCES OF INFORMATION.

6.3.1 General recommendations for typical houses

This list applies to most older houses with crawlspace foundations, regardless of the shape of the house.

1. Remove any masonry chimneys, or at least place plywood or OSB on top of ceiling joists in the attic adjacent to the chimney to help prevent bricks from showering through your ceiling during an earthquake (nailing the plywood to existing framing could change the way your home behaves in an earthquake, and is not recommended). You can keep the fireplace and transition from the masonry to a new metal chimney, or replace the fireplace with a manufactured unit. Figure 145 shows the remains of a chimney. Note the top portion of the chimney still connected to the roof, waiting to fall in an aftershock. *__There is no practical, affordable way to effectively retrofit a masonry chimney__*.
2. Anchor the mudsills to the footings.
3. If you have cripple walls, install shear panels. NOTE: The only reason that this item is listed after anchoring the mudsills is because once you install shear panels you have fewer options for anchoring the mudsills.
4. Install shear transfer ties.

Figure 145
The Northridge earthquake knocked over this chimney and thousands like it, even when they had been anchored according to the code when they were built. (FEMA photo by Andrea Booher)

6.3.2 Recommendations for long narrow houses

Many older homes were built on relatively narrow lots (40 feet was a common lot width a hundred years ago). Put a driveway along one side that leads to the carriage house in the rear, and you could end up with a 20-foot wide house, maybe 60 feet long.

Generally speaking, an earthquake could produce the same amount of force on your house acting from side to side as from front to rear. A long, narrow house is much stronger in the long direction, though, so if you have limited resources for retrofitting, it would be better to strengthen the narrow walls first. A detailed priority list might be as follows:

1. Remove masonry chimneys.
2. Mudsill anchors, shear panels and shear transfer ties on the narrow walls (typically the front and rear walls).
3. Mudsill anchors and shear panels on the long walls.
4. Shear transfer ties on the long walls.

There are two reasons that shear transfer ties on the long walls become a lower priority in a long house. First, the floor joists almost always span across the short dimension and bear on the long exterior walls in such houses. The joists are typically nailed to the cripple wall top plates with two or three large common nails. For joists spaced at 24 inches, this works out to one nail every 8 or 12 inches on average. (Contrast this to the narrow walls, where a joist runs parallel to the cripple wall and may only have toe-nails to the cripple wall top plate every few feet.) Closer joist spacings will provide even greater strength. We can be fairly certain that there are more nails per foot of wall length along the long walls than along the narrow walls. The second reason is simply that the long walls are just that—long. Each foot of wall length gives you more strength to resist earthquake forces.

6.3.3 Inspect, evaluate and improve existing retrofit work

Even if your house has been retrofitted, it is a good idea to have the installation checked and evaluated. Engineers and contractors continue to develop retrofit methods. With each earthquake we also learn which particular retrofit methods worked well and which ones to avoid. New hardware available in the last 15 years could also improve existing retrofits.

Often, a contractor installed all the retrofit measures that a homeowner could afford. This does not mean the retrofit is bad, simply that more work would improve its performance. It is better to start with some of the work discussed here than to wait until you save enough money for a "complete" retrofit.

In some cases, retrofits will just not perform well because they use ineffective methods. The following section discusses some of these.

INEFFECTIVE RETROFIT METHODS TO AVOID

Unfortunately, many misunderstandings have taken hold in the retrofit world, and many people have spent money on retrofit schemes that have little or no value in protecting structures. We feel it is important to present the most common of these questionable practices, so that owners know what *not* to spend their money on.

You do not want to pay for a retrofit that will not protect your home. Unfortunately, there are many, many instances of ineffective retrofit installations. The installations can look really sturdy—until you know the reasons that they are ineffective.

6.4.1 Interior posts typically do not need supplemental connections to beams

As discussed earlier, most earthquake damage occurs when houses move from side to side. Interior posts and beams that support a floor will typically stay in place and continue to function as long as the house does not slide off its footings. Typical steel connectors manufactured for post-to-beam attachment provide almost no strength to resist lateral forces that lead to most earthquake damage. With the exception of posts that provide the only support for a large building segment (or the whole building), this type of connection is usually not worth the money. Even for new construction the current code only requires a "positive connection" from a post to a beam; this could simply be a 2 x 4 or plywood scab on both sides of the joint (some jurisdictions may not allow toenails as a positive connection).

6.4.2 Adding tie-downs from interior footing piers to posts is ineffective

As mentioned in the previous section, we are not concerned much with upward movement of interior posts that support the floor framing. Connecting the posts to the piers they rest on is a very low priority. Some existing retrofits include tie-downs from cripple posts to isolated footings. Such a connection is not economical; even if we did need to keep the post in place, the tie-down can provide no more uplift resistance than the weight of the concrete pier. Piers are typically 12 inches square, and *maybe* 12 inches deep—often only 4 to 6 inches deep. A pier like this weighs no more than 150 pounds, which, along with some force due to soil adhesion, is the practical limit of uplift resistance that this connection will provide. Such connections are not even required for new construction under current codes.

6.4.3 "Hurricane ties" and other hardware designed to resist uplift provide very little strength to resist earthquake forces

Hurricanes produce large uplift forces as well as lateral forces. To repeat, earthquakes cause most damage by moving side to side. The strap shown in Figure 146 is designed by the manufacturer to resist uplift. The manufacturer's catalog does not list an allowable load for this connector acting as a shear transfer tie; therefore the allowable load for this connection is zero in the direction it needs to resist earthquake forces. The connection shown is completely ineffective; this condition requires not only proper mudsill anchors, but also shear panels on the cripple wall.

Figure 146

This connector is rated by its manufacturer only for uplift forces; it is useless in this installation for resisting lateral earthquake forces. (Photo courtesy of Roger Robinson, www.stargroup.com)

6.4.4 Beware of angle-iron "levers"

The vertical angle-iron shown in Figure 147 looks *really strong*, and it is—but its strength is not useful when installed in this manner. We need to resist lateral forces acting in the direction along the foundation wall. If the floor joist exerts a lateral force at the top of the steel angle shown, the steel angle acts as a lever. The lever action does two things: it will twist the joist over, and it will break the old, weak concrete footing. Most engineers would look at this connection and just shake their heads in disbelief, but one engineer did actually take the time to calculate what a similar connection could resist; the conclusion was that the specific connection checked could safely resist about 300 to 400 pounds parallel to the foundation wall (note that depending on the geometry, the connection could be stronger or weaker than this calculated figure). Some engineers feel that angle irons installed in this manner will do more harm than good, and recommend removing them. The installation shown costs roughly the same as a "UFP10" or similar, but to match a UFP10's strength requires many angle-irons and project-specific engineering.

Figure 147

This piece of angle-iron is very strong. Unfortunately the way it is installed is virtually useless for resisting earthquake forces. (Photo courtesy of Roger Robinson, www.stargroup.com)

The other purpose that the angle iron connection could serve is to hold the house down on the footings—but as discussed before, we are less concerned about uplift than lateral forces.

"Home-made" connections like this angle-iron have not been tested for any load rating (although thousands of them will be tested by an earthquake eventually). Using manufactured hardware components that have a code-accepted load rating gives much more reliability.

Even properly engineered and installed angle-irons must be analyzed for each particular installation. This becomes problematic when an existing retrofit is being reviewed and evaluated. It is often more costly to analyze existing angle-irons than it is to simply install new retrofit hardware as described in Section 6.2.2.2.

Note that there is an acceptable purpose for angle-iron connectors in anchoring hillside homes (see Section 6.5.2) to the uphill footing. These installations should have site-specific engineered solutions, however, which are far beyond the scope of this chapter.

6.4.5 Isolated braces may cause localized damage at connections

Some retrofits include diagonal braces from floor joists down to the footing. These braces were often installed in cases where there was no footing under the front wall of a house (see the first bullet item under Section 6.5.1) and the owner could not afford to have a new footing and sheathed cripple wall installed. The diagonal braces will exert concentrated loads on the joists during an earthquake, which could overload the joist (especially when combined with floor loads). This sort of installation was a good initial step toward a retrofit, but if you can afford to replace it with a new footing and shear wall you should do so.

Other problems with such an installation include:

- If the connection to the floor joist fails, the brace could punch up through the floor if the cripple walls collapse and the house falls.

- Depending on the length of the brace, it could buckle under compressive loads.

- The braces often obstruct the crawlspace; if they are not recognized as important structural elements by future tradesworkers, they could be cut or removed to install future utilities.

6.4.6 Adding connectors from the underside of the floor sheathing to the floor framing is very seldom necessary

Additional connectors from the boundary members of the existing floor diaphragm to the cripple walls (or directly to the mudsill, when no cripple wall is present) may be necessary, as discussed in Section 6.2.1. Shear transfer ties connect the floor *framing* to the cripple walls—but what about the floor sheathing connection to the framing? The subflooring in typical older wood-framed buildings has two or three nails from each sheathing board to the end joists, rim joists or blocking. As discussed in Section 1.2, the forces in the floor diaphragm are spread out over a large area. When the forces are spread out this way the existing connections from floor sheathing to floor framing are almost always adequate to transfer earthquake forces into the framing below.

The IEBC gives strength values in Table A1-D that engineers can use for typical materials found in old buildings. Any of the materials listed are generally strong enough to transfer diaphragm forces from the existing floor sheathing to the floor framing. Floor sheathing connections hardly ever need additional fastening in a typical residence.

ISSUES NOT ADDRESSED HERE

See the disclaimer at the beginning of this chapter! Unusually shaped homes, narrow multistory homes that have a garage door across most of the width of the ground floor, homes built on steep hillsides, etc., are beyond the scope of these recommendations. Likewise, poor connections of porch roofs (which often have many layers of roofing built up on them) and other structural components can pose significant hazards. If you live in a home with any of these or related problems, seriously consider buying earthquake insurance or having your house retrofitted by a contractor experienced in retrofit work, based on a design by an engineer with expertise in this specialty.

6.5.1 Cripple wall and other crawlspace problems

Retrofit shear walls present many different scenarios. Work is underway on a separate publication that will thoroughly cover as many of these cases as possible. Some retrofit concerns not mentioned above include the following (if the house you are retrofitting includes any of these items, you may wish to consult an expert in earthquake retrofits):

- No cripple wall or continuous footing present under the front wall of the house—this is very common in houses that have a front porch, where the cripple wall is at the front of the porch and the front house wall is supported by a row of posts set on concrete piers.

- Existing utilities and other obstacles that obstruct installation of retrofit components—many homes that need retrofitting were built before indoor plumbing and modern heating systems were in widespread use, or had very limited plumbing and mechanical systems. Most homes had plumbing and heating upgrades installed decades later, and those systems block access to the structure.

- Pest damage—if termites or rot have consumed structural members, attaching retrofit components to them is pointless. Previous pest control work may also have compromised the original structure's integrity—often the infested wood is simply cut out and replaced, with little thought given to maintaining lateral load paths in the house.

- Severely cracked or otherwise deteriorating concrete or masonry footings—if the existing footings are in such poor condition that new mudsill connections will not be effective, you will not get the full benefits of a retrofit without repairing or replacing the footings. Foundation repairs can add huge expense to a retrofit; if you cannot afford this work, you will very likely still benefit from other retrofit installations recommended in this chapter.

- Provisions for tie-down forces—as cripple wall heights increase, so does the need for tie-downs at the ends of retrofit shear walls.

6.5.2 Hillside homes with tall posts or tall walls on the downhill side

Hillside homes on the downhill side of the street are often supported on tall posts or walls on the downhill side. These homes often fare poorly in earthquakes, as shown in Figure 148.

Retrofitting hillside houses requires anchoring for the entire side-wall reaction force to the footing at the uphill end of the wall. Such a connection is shown in Figure 140.

Figure 148
The photo above shows a hillside home that was utterly destroyed by the 1989 Loma Prieta earthquake. (FEMA photo by JK Nakata)

Chapter 7

CONCLUSIONS AND RECOMMENDATIONS

As we have seen, shear walls and the related components of buildings can quickly become complicated in today's homes. A shear element looks very simple in engineering text books—just a square with forces acting along each edge. Constructing shear walls in the field requires attention to many details just for a simple rectangular wall. Throw in problems such as holes for ductwork or windows, stepped footings, and forces that must travel through the structure before they get to the shear wall, and you get some very complicated structural systems. Viewing each shear wall—or even each sheet of shear paneling—as a shear element can help you build a complete lateral force resisting system.

Just as a simple shear element must have equal and opposite forces on each side, so must a shear wall. Start at the top of the wall. Does the diaphragm above have a way to transfer the "action" force into the shear wall? Can the force from a collector get transferred into the wall whether the collector is in tension or in compression? Now check the bottom of the wall. Do the connections from the sill or sole plate have the strength to transfer the shear force into the structure below? Then check to see that both ends of the wall can resist vertical forces. Do the end-posts bear solidly on framing or concrete so that they can handle downward forces? Is there a tie-down present to resist upward forces? (Sometimes the weight of the structure is sufficient to prevent the wall from lifting up off its foundation so that tie-downs are not always needed.) Finally, verify that the wall has sufficient strength to resist the forces exerted along each of its edges, and along each edge of each panel from which it is built.

Researchers continue to learn about shear wall behavior. After every earthquake or severe storm engineers study buildings that suffered damage and try to determine what failed, how designs could be improved, what materials perform well, and so forth.

The website at www.shearwalls.com will include important research results, building code amendments and so forth, as they become available. This will allow much speedier updates than print media. Perhaps the most important thing to remember is what *won't* change: The underlying principles of physics that make shear walls necessary.

FIELD INSPECTION CHECKLIST

Based on 2009 IBC Table 2306.4.1

OVERVIEW:

Shear walls serve a critical role in protecting the safety of building occupants during windstorms or earthquakes. Careful construction and inspection of shear walls is very important. A single defect in a shear wall can greatly reduce the whole wall's performance.

Every edge of every piece of shear wall sheathing must connect to a structural element. Boundary elements on all sides of the shear wall must also attach to the framing above or to the structure below. The top of the shear wall will typically connect to eave or joist blocking, a roof truss, end rafter or joist. The posts at either end of a shear wall typically connect to the framing or footing below with a tie-down bracket or strap. The sole plate connects to framing below with extra nails, lag bolts, structural screws, etc. Where the bottom plate of the shear wall bears on a footing it may need more anchor bolts than otherwise required.

Develop a routine for inspecting shear walls. A possible sequence is as follows: Check all the sheathing nailing, around one piece of sheathing at a time. Next, verify that the top of the shear wall is connected adequately to the framing above; then check to see that the end posts are properly anchored. Finally, check to see that the bottom of the shear wall is secured to the framing or footing below to form a continuous load path to the foundation.

The following sections detail many individual requirements. Not all of the following items will apply to every shear wall installation, and some installations may include items not mentioned in the following list.

SPECIFIC REQUIREMENTS:

1. **Verify lengths of all shear walls on framing or floor plans.**

   ☐ The length of a shear wall is measured as the sheathed dimension.

2. **Verify shear transfer connections and anchorage at sill/sole plate conforms to plans:**

   ☐ Nail size and spacing at sole plate to floor framing below in accordance with shear wall schedule (verify nails penetrate framing below)

   ☐ Foundation anchor bolt diameter, spacing or number of bolts is in accordance with foundation plan, shear wall schedule or structural notes

   ☐ Foundation anchor bolts are not less than 7 bolt diameters ($3^1/_2$ inches for $^1/_2$ diameter bolts, $4 ^3/_8$ inches for $^5/_8$ inch diameter bolts, $5 ^1/_4$ inch for $^3/_4$ inch bolts from end of sill plate piece and not more than 12 inches from ends. Note: Minimum end distance of 12 bolt diameters is preferred.

   ☐ Foundation anchor bolts are not less than 1.5 bolt diameters ($^3/_4$ inch for $^1/_2$ inch bolts, $^{15}/_{16}$ inch for $^5/_8$ inch bolts, $1 ^1/_8$ inch for $^3/_4$ inch bolts) from centerline of bolt to the edge of the sill plate

   ☐ Foundation anchor bolt distance from edge and end of concrete foundation conforms to the plans. If not specified, $1^1/_2$ inch minimum clearance is required between steel and face of concrete.

   ☐ Foundation sill material is compatible with fasteners. Lumber treated with ACQ and other copper-containing compounds can corrode even galvanized fasteners very aggressively. Borate-treated lumber is much less corrosive than ACQ and other treatments.

   ☐ Anchor bolt holes in sill plates are not more than $^1/_{16}$ inch larger than actual bolt diameter (for over-sized holes, fill gap between bolt and sill with epoxy or non-shrink grout).

   ☐ Anchor bolts extend far enough out of concrete so that sill does not have to be notched to install required nut and washer(s).

   ☐ Steel plate washers, a minimum of 0.229 inch thick by 3 inches square between the sill plate and nut as required by the plans.

   ☐ Diagonally slotted hole in the plate washer is permitted with a width of up to the bolt diameter $+ ^3/_{16}$ inch and a slot length not greater than $1^3/_4$ inches with a standard cut (round) washer between the plate washer and nut.

   ☐ Edge of plate washer extends to within $^1/_2$-inch of shear panel.

3. Verify hold down installation where required by the plans:

☐ Prior to pouring concrete foundation, verify that embedment lengths of tie down anchor rods conform to the plans.

☐ Prior to pouring concrete foundation, verify that type of embedded end of anchor rods (L hook, J hook, nut and square plate, hex headed bolt) conform to the plans.

☐ Foundation reinforcement and footing size at shear walls and tie-downs conform to the plans.

☐ Tie-down device anchor rod edge and end distances conform to the plans.

☐ Tie-downs are usually (but not always) required at each end of each shear wall.

☐ Location of tie-downs in accordance with foundation or framing plans.

☐ Minimum post size at tie-down in accordance with plans.

☐ Tie-down device must connect directly to post, without spacers or shims.

☐ Multiple studs used as end-posts must be adequately connected (requires more than just the fasteners that connect the tie-down to the post). Verify fastening of multiple studs is in accordance with plans.

☐ For bolted tie-down brackets, verify diameter of bolt holes through shear wall end-post are not more than $1/16$ inch larger than actual bolt diameter.

☐ All required fasteners are installed from tie-down to post and are of the size specified by the manufacturer or specified on the plans (note that tie-downs can also use nails, self-drilling screws or other types of fasteners).

☐ All bolt sizes meet the tie-down manufacturer's requirements or conform to the plans.

☐ Bolt heads or nuts are not countersunk into post unless specifically indicated on plans.

☐ For tie-downs bolted to end-posts, nuts are on the side of the post away from the tie-down if required by the manufacturer.

☐ Washer is installed under the nut on the side of the post opposite the tie- down device (square bearing plate washers if required by local codes).

☐ Nuts are tight on all tie-down bolts through shear wall end-posts.

☐ Nuts are tight on all foundation anchor rods.

☐ Nuts are tight on all threaded rods that span from lower floor to upper floor.

☐ Anchor rods and threaded rods are straight and not bent or bowed.

☐ An equal number of nails are used in upper and lower wall framing for strap-type tie-downs that span from lower floor to upper floor unless shown otherwise on the plans.

☐ Straps are straight, not bent to follow jogs in framing.

☐ Notches or large holes are not permitted in end-posts unless specifically shown on the plans.

☐ Verify proper installation of shrinkage-compensating devices where specified, in accordance with manufacturer's recommendations and the plans.

4. Verify wood framing lumber size and grade conforms to the plans:

☐ Two-inch nominal or wider framing is required at all panel edges.

☐ Framing size at panel joints: If required on the plans, verify 3x studs at abutting panel joints, doubled 2x studs fastened together, single 3x foundation sill, etc. For doubled 2x studs, the studs must be securely fastened together (typically with 16d commons at the same spacing as the panel edge nailing).

☐ Framing lumber species (Douglas Fir-Larch, Southern Pine, etc.)

☐ Framing lumber grade at intermediate studs and end-posts (Stud, Construction, No.2, No. 1, etc.) conform to the plans.

5. Support under shear wall end-posts:

☐ Verify full bearing of end-post on foundation sill plate, metal post-base or sole plate.

☐ At framed floors, verify full blocking or other bearing members under posts.

6. Verify that sheathing fasteners conform to the plans or shear wall schedule:

☐ Fastener type (nail or staple). NOTE: staples are not recommended in high seismic areas.

☐ Fastener compatibility with treated lumber; if foundation sill or other members are treated with CA, CC, ACZA, ACQ or other copper-based preservatives, all fasteners driven into the treated lumber must be hot-dipped galvanized; stainless steel is highly recommended. Borate-treated lumber does not require special fasteners.

☐ Nail style (common, galvanized box).

☐ Nail size (6d, 8d, 10d) or actual diameter and length as noted on planes.

☐ For 10-penny nails, "plywood" nails are preferred. (Plywood nails are gun nails with lengths of $2^1/_8$ to $2^3/_8$ inches rather than 3 inches; they are *not* 'teco' or joist hanger nails.) Plywood nails do not tend to split the framing as much as common nails.

☐ Nail head shape (clipped heads may not be permitted).

☐ Galvanized nails are hot dipped or tumbled, not electroplated.

☐ Where allowed, staples have $^7/_{16}$ inch crown width minimum and crown installed parallel to grain of framing member.

☐ Fastener spacing at all edges of sheathing (6 inch o.c, 4 inch o.c, 3 inch o.c., 2 inch o.c.) If nails are spaced at less than the required spacing, check that the framing members have not been split.

☐ Fastener placement.

☐ Fasteners are driven flush and not overdriven. (Note: Where nails are overdriven, follow APA guidelines, Form TT-012.)

☐ Minimum $^3/_8$ inch from edge of sheathing to center of fastener.

☐ Nails (staples) are embedded firmly into framing members. Inspect stud side for "shiners" (nails that missed the framing).

☐ Nails of any size are staggered along edges where nail spacing is 2 inches.

☐ 10d nails are staggered along edges where spacing is 3 inches or less.

☐ Sheathing is fastened to tie-down post at required "edge nail" spacing.

☐ For "Type 303 Siding" ("T1-11", grooved siding, reverse board and batten, etc.) nails are required on both sides of panel joints, not just the overlapping panel.

7. Verify wood structural panel sheathing conforms to plans:

☐ Sheathing type (plywood, OSB or composite panels).

☐ Sheathing grade (for example: Sheathing, Plywood Siding, Structural I, APA Rated Panel).

☐ Panel thickness ($^5/_{16}$ inch, $^3/_8$ inch, $^7/_{16}$ inch, $^{15}/_{32}$ inch, $^{19}/_{32}$ inch). For grooved siding, the thickness considered is the thickness that the fasteners are driven through.

☐ Number of plies (where specified for plywood panels).

☐ Where specified, panels must be installed with their face-grain horizontal (perpendicular to the studs).

☐ Gaps at abutting panel joints in exterior walls to allow for expansion, as required by panel manufacturer.

☐ Shear panels attached directly to studs. Where fire-resistive construction is required, gypsum board should be installed after the shear panels; in this case gypsum board fastener length shall be increased by the shear panel thickness.

☐ Holes in shear panels must be cut neatly, without overcuts. Slots are not allowed (such as to slide shear panels over existing obstructions).

8. Verify shear transfer connections at top of wall at roof or floor level above:

☐ Location, size and spacing of edge nailing from sheathing to top plate of shear wall.

☐ Shear panels may run beyond plate or sill to lap onto rim joist or blocking, with nailing to the joist or blocking.

☐ Location, type and spacing of framing anchors (where required) from top plate to roof or floor framing or blocking with all nail holes filled (unless otherwise noted on approved plans)

☐ For interior shear walls parallel to framing, shear panels must extend to underside of the floor or roof sheathing above, or to a collector.

☐ For joists or rafters perpendicular to shear walls below, solid blocking must be installed above the shear wall; for trusses perpendicular to wall, "blocking frames" or similar are needed between the trusses. In all cases, the floor or roof sheathing must be nailed to the blocks or frames at specified spacing. (See Figures 20-22 and 24-26 in *"Wood-Framed Shear Wall Construction—an Illustrated Guide"*)
[Note: In some cases floor sheathing nailing to top plates of shear walls (or to blocking, collectors, etc.) must be inspected before subsequent construction covers it up].

☐ Gable-end walls must be sheathed all the way up and onto the end rafter or truss top chord unless truss engineering justifies transfer of lateral load through truss from the top chord to the bottom chord.

9. Verify top plate splice connection along shear wall lines, diaphragm boundaries and collectors:

☐ Check plans for typical top plate splice connection or special plate splices such as straps or increased nailing.

☐ Splice connections are needed at plate joints or interruptions.

☐ Where straps are used to splice plates, verify strap size (gage, thickness, length), number of rows of nails, and total number of nails in accordance with manufacturer's specifications.

☐ Verify that straps are centered on splice joint and all nail holes are filled (unless otherwise noted on plans).

REFERENCES

SUGGESTED READING

General:

Graphic Guide to Frame Construction, Taunton Press

Seismic Detailing Examples for Engineered Light-Frame Timber Construction, Structural Engineers Association of San Diego

For Earthquake Retrofits:

International Existing Building Code (IEBC) International Code Council, www.iccsafe.org

Plan Set A; http://www.quake.abag.ca.gov/wp-content/documents/Plan-Set-A.pdf

"Earthquake Home Retrofit Handbook" City of Seattle, Washington; www.seattle.gov/emergency/library/mitigation/HR%20Book%202%20-%20assessment.pdf

"Standard Earthquake Home Retrofit Plan Set"; City of Seattle, Washington; www.cityofseattle.net/dpd/static/20_pages_LatestReleased_DPDP_021980.pdf

"Standard Plan No. 1"; Los Angeles Department of Building and Safety, www.ci.la.ca.us/ladbs/rpt_code_pub/anchor_bolting.pdf

CITED REFERENCES

[1] John Henry. 2001. "Special Inspection, Structural Observation and Quality Assurance Under the 2000 IBC." *Building Standards*, ICBO, May/June 2001.

[2] Robert Reitherman. 2000. "The CUREe-CalTech Woodframe Project." *Structure*, National Council of Structural Engineers Associations-Council of American Structural Engineers-Structural Engineering Institute, (winter, 2000).

[3] U.S. Geological Survey, Earthquake Hazards Program, National Seismic Hazard Mapping Project http://www.earthquake.usgs.gov/hazards

[4] HAZUS 99: Average Annual Earthquake Losses for the United States, Federal Emergency Management Agency (FEMA). (superseded, see www.fema.gov/plan/prevent/hazus)

[5] CUREe-Caltech Woodframe Project Newsletter, No. 1, 1998; Consortium of Universities for Research in Earthquake Engineering (CUREe), November, 1998.

[6] Bossi, Robert J. and Kelly E. Cobeen. 1996. "Conventional Construction for Today's Buildings." *Building Standards*, ICBO, September/October 1996.

[7] *Standard for Residential Construction in High-Wind Regions,* ICC 600-2008, International Code Council, Whittier, CA. ISBN 9781580017473.

[8] Report 154. "Wood Structural Panel Shear Walls," Form No. Q260C. 1999. APA—The Engineered Wood Association, Tacoma, WA. www.apawood.org

[9] Report 158. "Preliminary Testing of Wood Structural Panel Shear Walls Under Cyclic (Reversed) Loading," Form No. W260A. 1999. APA—The Engineered Wood Association. Tacoma, WA. www.apawood.org

[10] ESR-1539, Evaluation Service Report, 2009 ICC Evaluation Service, Inc., Whittier, CA. www.icc-es.org/reports/pdf_files/icc-es/esr-1539.pdf

[11] Form No. TT012, APA—the Engineered Wood Association, Technical Services Division, October 2002, Tacoma, WA. www.apawood.org

[12] "Design/Construction Guide—Diaphragms and Shear Walls," Form No. L350F. 1997. APA—The Engineered Wood Association; www.apawood.org

[13] Resisting the Forces of Earthquakes. Earthquake Engineering Research Institute, Oakland, CA, video. EERI, 499 14th St, Oakland, CA 94612; www.eeri.org

[14] EQE Project No. 200674.01 1999. "Results of Cyclic (Reversed) Load Testing for Shear Resistance of Wood Framed Plywood Shear Walls with USP lumber Connector Hold-Downs, SEAOSC Testing Protocol 9/97." EQE International, December 13, Irvine, CA.

[15] "Sturd-I-Frames for Narrow Wall Bracing," Form No. B440. 2001. APA—The Engineered Wood Association (discontinued—see Form G440 and Form TT-100) www.apawood.org

[16] Alfred Commins. 2001. "Wood Shrinkage and Shear Wall Performance." *Building Standards*, ICBO, November/December 2001.

[17] "Introduction to Lateral Design," Form No. X305A. 1999. APA—The Engineered Wood Association. www.apawood.org/pdfs/download_pdf.cfm?PDFFilename=managed/x305.pdf

[18] ANSI/AF&PA "Special Design Provisions for Wind and Seismic" 2005 (SDPWS), American National Standards Institute/American Forest & Paper Association, American Wood Council, 1111 Nineteenth St. NW, Ste. 800, Washington, DC 20036; www.afandpa.org

[19] American Society of Civil Engineers, ASCE-7. "Minimum Design Loads for Buildings and Other Structures", American Society of Civil Engineers, 1801 Alexander Bell Drive, Reston, VA 20191; www.asce.org

[20] *Plan Set A*; Association of Bay Area Governments (ABAG), et al. http://www.quake.abag.ca.gov/wp-content/documents/Plan-Set-A.pdf

[21] "Seismic Behavior of Level and Stepped Cripple Walls;" CUREE-CalTech Woodframe Project Report W-17; Chai, Rob YH, T. Hutchinson, S. Vukazich; CUREE-Caltech Wood-Frame Project; www.curee.org

MANUFACTURERS

TIE-DOWNS, CONNECTORS AND OTHER HARDWARE

Cleveland Steel Specialty Company
26001 Richmond Rd.
Bedford Heights, OH 44146
(800) 251-8351
www.clevelandsteel.com
Tie-downs, framing connectors and other hardware

Commins Manufacturing
P.O.Box 3338, Friday Harbor, WA 98250
(360) 378-9484
www.comminsmfg.com
Shrinkage compensating devices

Earthbound Corporation
17361 Tye Street SE Monroe, WA 98272
(360)-863-0722 or (800)-944-5669
www.holdown.com
"Earthbound" high-capacity, continuous tie-down system, Standard and high-strength
threaded rod and couplers, "Slackjack" shrinkage compensating devices

K-C Metals
1960 Hartog Drive, San Jose, CA 95131
(408) 436-8754
www.kcmetals.com
Tie-downs, straps and other hardware

Simpson Strong-Tie Company
Home Office: P.O. Box 10789, Pleasanton, CA 94588
(800) 999-5099
www.strongtie.com
Tie-downs, straps and other hardware, Shrinkage compensating devices

USP Lumber Connectors
Corporate Office: 703 Rogers Drive, Montgomery, MN 56069-1324
(800) 328-5934
www.uspconnectors.com;
Tie-downs, straps and other hardware

Zone Four
31945 Corydon Rd - Lake Elsinore - CA 92530
(877)-432-4444
www.zonefour.com
High-capacity, continuous tie-downs and other hardware, Shrinkage compensating devices
(manufactured by Commins Mfg.)

PREFABRICATED SHEAR WALLS OR BRACING PANELS

EZTech
P. O. Box 3337, San Luis Obispo, CA 93405
(800) 735-5922
www.z-wall.net
"Z-Wall" diagonally braced steel frames

I-Level (formerly Weyerhauser)
200 E. Mallard Drive, Boise, ID 83706
(888) 453-8358
http://www.ilevel.com/walls/w_Shear-Brace.aspx
"iLevel Shear Brace" engineered wood panel; essentially a wide "I" joist stood on end with integral tie-downs at each end (this system was formerly manufactured by Trus-joist under the name "TJ-Shear Panel")

Shear Transfer Systems
P.O. Box 402563, Hesperia, CA 92340-2563
(877) 743-2762
www.shearmax.com
"Shear Max" wood studs with OSB face panel

Simplified Structural Systems (a division of Mitek Industries)
789 S. Victoria Ave. #200, Ventura, CA 93003
(800) 754-3030
www.hardyframe.com
"Hardy-Frame" diagonally braced steel stud panel; "Hardy-Panel," steel studs with steel face panel

Simpson Strong-Tie Company
Home Office: P.O. Box 10789, Pleasanton, CA 94588
(800) 999-5099
http://www.strongtie.com/products/strongwall/index.html
 "Strong-Wall" wood studs with OSB face panel

WellBilt International
8600 NW South River Drive, Miami, Florida 33166 USA
(305) 884-8020
http://www.sureboard.com/
"Sure-board" panels (22-gage steel bonded to gypsum board or other substrate). These panels may be used in an engineered design only; the current information on the company's website suggests that using their product can eliminate the need for shear walls. Engineering would still be required in order to use the product; whether you call it a "shear wall" or a "Sure-Board wall" it must still be engineered to resist the same physical forces.

GLOSSARY

Anchor bolt
Also called "J-bolt," or "L-bolt," depending on its shape; used to connect sill plates to footings. The term "bolt" technically means a headed fastener; thus, "anchor bolt" is not entirely accurate to describe typical sill anchors.

Anchor rod
Used in this book to describe hardware that connects a tie-down to the footing. "Anchor rod" is a more technically accurate term to describe a threaded fastener that connects a building's superstructure to the footing (see entry above).

APA
Formerly The American Plywood Association; changed its name to "APA—The Engineered Wood Association."

Boundary
An edge of a diaphragm; typically along eave blocking and the trusses or rafters in line with the gable-end walls for a roof diaphragm (not the fascia or barge rafters), the end and rim (band) joists for a floor diaphragm and the end-posts and top and bottom members of a shear wall.

Chord
The top or bottom member of a truss; also used to describe the member along a diaphragm boundary (diaphragm chord).

Collector
A structural member that connects a diaphragm to a shear wall in order to gather lateral forces spread throughout the diaphragm and deliver them to the shear wall.

Cripple wall
A short wood-framed wall built on top of the foundation to support framing for the first-floor level above.

Diaphragm
A large area of sheathing such as a floor, roof or shear wall (diaphragms may be vertical as well as horizontal); in order to function as a diaphragm, all edges of the sheathed area must have boundary members, and the sheathing panels must connect to these members and to intermediate framing members to transfer forces across the panel joints.

Double plate
Two horizontal framing members at the top of a wall, typically spliced or lapped to give continuity or tie wall sections together.

Drag strut
Essentially the same as a collector; may have slightly varying meanings, such as a collector that only functions in compression.

Drag tie
Essentially the same as a drag strut or collector, with the added possibility that it may refer to a member that only transmits force from one part of the structure to another part some distance away, without collecting any additional force along the way.

Edge
When referring to a shear panel, a panel has four edges—two of these edges are "ends" and two are "sides."

ESR
Evaluation Service Report—a report issued by ICC Evaluation Services.

ESR-1539
Evaluation Service Report 1539 lists strength values for various connectors based on data from the International Staple, Nail and Tool Association (ISANTA).

Header
A horizontal member that spans across an opening in a wall (typically over a door or window).

Hold-down
See "Tie-down" — a device used to keep the end of a shear wall from lifting up.

IBC
International Building Code; published by the International Code Council, Inc., and available for adoption by government jurisdictions internationally.

ICBO
International Conference of Building Officials; publisher of the *Uniform Building Code*. The ICBO is one of the three model code organizations that became the International Code Council (ICC).

ICC
International Code Council; publisher of the *International Codes*; including the *International Building Code* and the *International Residential Code*.

ICC ES
ICC Evaluation Service— an organization that evaluates materials, products and systems to meet the requirements of the various building codes. ES reports detail installation requirements and limitations that are necessary for code compliance. ICC ES is a subsidiary of the ICC.

ISANTA
The International Staple, Nail and Tool Association.

IRC
International Residential Code; a code for one- and two-family dwellings published by the ICC.

King stud
A stud that extends up from the bottom plate to the top plate of a wall and connects to the end of a header.

Lateral
Describing forces that act in a horizontal direction; usually caused by wind or earthquakes.

Mudsill
As used in this guide, same as sill; sometimes referred to as "foundation sill".

NER-272
An obsolete National Evaluation Report issued by the National Evaluation Service for power-driven nails and staples. This report has been replaced by ESR-1539.

APPENDIX B

ENGINEERING PRINCIPLES OF SHEAR WALLS WITH SLOPING TOP PLATES

APA—The Engineered Wood Association and others have tested only rectangular shear wall assemblies. Most of these have been 8 feet high and 8 feet wide, with more recent tests also involving 4-foot-wide walls. What happens when the top and bottom members of the shear wall are not parallel? We can no longer divide the wall into square elements that carry only shear forces along each edge. If we have a fully sheathed gable end wall, then it may be safe to assume that the symmetry of the wall will carry diaphragm forces to the rectangular portion of the shear wall below. Many times, though, the shear wall or shear wall segment only slopes in one direction, as shown in Figures 17 and 150.

Designers sometimes "simplify" the overturning and tie-down force calculations for a sloped wall by assuming that the total force on the wall acts horizontally at the average wall height. This simplification is incorrect and can lead to seriously underestimated tie-down forces. An analysis of a mono-sloped shear wall follows.

Figure 150
Shear-wall segments with mono-sloped top plates.

By definition, the roof diaphragm only carries forces within the plane of the sheathing. Therefore, the force delivered from the diaphragm acts along the sloping top member of the shear wall. Figure 151 shows a free-body diagram of a shear wall with a sloping top. The figure illustrates how the diaphragm force creates a greater overturning moment (OTM) about the base of the taller end-post than it does about the base of the shorter end-post. Because the same distance between the end-posts is used to find the tie-down force at either end of the wall, we find that the tie-down force at the short end-post is always greater than that at the tall end-post. (Note that in this discussion we will focus on the tie-down forces; the compressive forces in the end-posts will have the same relationship in the case where the load at the top of the wall reverses.)

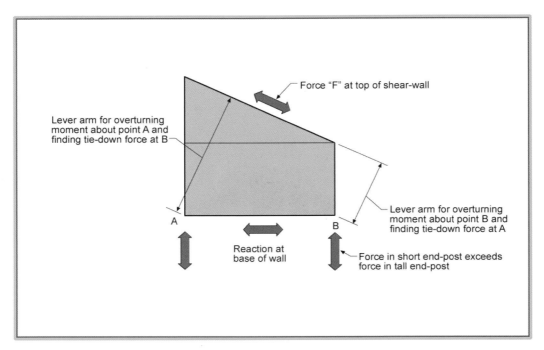

Figure 151
Schematic free-body diagram of shear wall with sloped top plate.

Figure 152 shows an example of a sloping shear wall with actual dimensions and forces.

Finding the OTM about Point A, we get

$(OTM)_A$ = 12.93 feet (2,500 pounds) = 32,320 foot-pounds

From this we can determine the tie-down force, T, at the short end-post (at Point B) as:

T_B = 32,320 foot-pounds/12 feet = 2,693 pounds

The OTM about Point B is:

$(OTM)_B$ = 6.93 feet (2,500 pounds) = 17,320 foot-pounds

Which gives the tie-down force at the tall end-post (Point A) as:

T_A = 17,320 foot-pounds/12 feet = 1,443 pounds

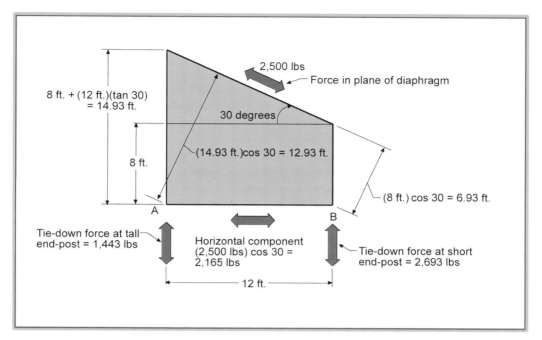

Figure 152
Example wall illustrating different tie-down forces at each end-post.

In this example, the tie-down force at the short end-post is almost twice that at the tall end-post.

If we assumed, incorrectly, that the diaphragm force acted horizontally at the average wall height, we would get the same tie-down force at each end of the wall of (11.47 feet) (2,500 pounds) (cos 30)/12 feet = 2,068 pounds). This is the *average* of the correct tie-down forces that act at each end-post.

If we break the sloped wall into two segments we can analyze them separately and better understand how the wall works as a whole. We have established that the diaphragm force acts parallel to, and along, the sloping top of the triangular wall segment. The reaction from the main (rectangular) portion of the wall acts horizontally on the bottom of the triangular segment. By the principles of statics, the triangular wall segment is a "three-force body." The third force must act through a point concurrent with the first two. This means that a vertical force must act at the intersection point of the sloping top plate and the horizontal wall plate. Figure 153 illustrates the triangular portion of the shear wall. The triangular segment of shear panels apparently acts as a huge gusset that connects the sloping and horizontal members. For the example in Figure 152, the forces would be as follows:

Horizontal reaction = (2,500 pounds) cos 30 = 2,165 pounds

Vertical reaction = (2,500 pounds) sin 30 = 1,250 pounds

This indicates that we must provide a tie-down force of 1,250 pounds to the sloped member of the triangular section of the shear wall. One way to accomplish this is by installing a strap from the short end-post up and over the sloping top member of the shear wall, as shown in Figure 135. We must remember that the additional vertical force component acts at the sloped top member of the shear wall. Simply increasing the tie-down connection to the base of the short end-post will allow the top portion of the wall to lift up and away.

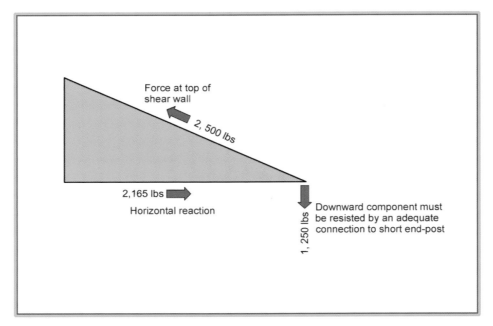

Force at top of
shear wall

2, 500 lbs

2,165 lbs ➡

Horizontal reaction

1, 250 lbs

Downward component must
be resisted by an adequate
connection to short end-post

Figure 153

Free-body diagram of triangular portion of wall. The lines of action of all three forces
must pass through the low point of the triangle.

If we consider only the rectangular portion of the wall, we can then add the vertical reaction
from the triangular portion to find the overall tie-down forces. Using the shear wall from the previous example, the horizontal component acting at the top of the rectangular portion of the wall
would require a tie-down force of (2,165 pounds) 8 feet/12 feet = 1,443 pounds. This is the
same force we found for the tall end-post as determined in Figure 152. If we add the
1,250-pound vertical component shown in Figure 153 to 1,443 pounds, we get 2,693 pounds.
This is the same force determined in Figure 152 as the tie-down force at the short end-post.

The preceding gives us another method to find the tie-down force at the short end-post: The
horizontal component of the diaphragm force (typically determined in a lateral analysis) multiplied by the tangent of the roof angle gives the vertical force required to tie the triangular wall
segment to the short end-post. Figure 154 illustrates how we can add the forces determined in
the "standard" rectangular wall and the triangular segment to get the overall forces on the wall.

Note that this is a theoretical analysis and does not account for the deformation of the wall segments, added strength from sloped rafters that may be present at the top of the wall, bending in
the nails, panel buckling, dead load of the wall and any tributary roof area, and so forth. Full
scale testing of mono-sloped wall segments could verify or disprove the assumptions stated
above. Until such testing is undertaken, this author recommends the preceding approach.
Once you get used to the process, it is just as easy as the more common approach of finding
the overturning moment due to a horizontal load applied at the average wall height. Calculating
the vertical component of force in the short end-post involves no more effort than finding the
average wall height.

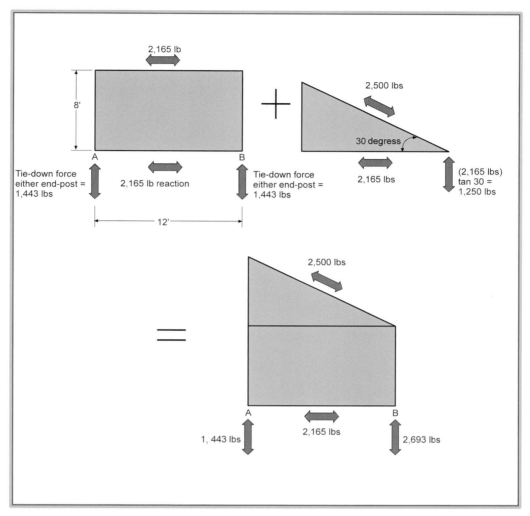

Figure 154
Example showing "super-position" of forces.

Readers may notice that the walls with sloping top plates shown in this section look similar to upside-down versions of the walls shown in Section 5.4.1. Why do we not worry about a shear wall with a sloped top, but we advise against shear walls with sloped bottoms? Primarily, if a shear wall attaches to a stepped footing, the shear wall framing and sheathing will be slammed violently against the steps in the footing during an earthquake. This does not occur in the case of a shear wall connected to a sloping roof diaphragm; the nonrectangular portion of the shear wall is connected to a much more flexible portion of the building than the footings. As noted above, this subject needs further study and testing to gain better understanding of the structural concerns regarding sloping shear walls.